FOUNDATION
SCiENCE to
GCSE

Stephen Pople

Oxford University Press, Great Clarendon Street, Oxford OX2 6DP

Oxford New York
Athens Auckland Bangkok Bogotá
Buenos Aires Calcutta Cape Town Chennai
Dar es Salaam Delhi Florence Honk Kong Istanbul
Karachi Kuala Lumpur Madrid Melbourne
Mexico City Mumbai Nairobi Paris São Paolo
Singapore Taipei Tokyo Toronto Warsaw
and associated companies in
Berlin Ibadan

Oxford is a trade mark of Oxford University Press

© Stephen Pople 1997

First published 1997
Reprinted 1998 (twice)
Reprinted 2001

A CIP catalogue record for this book is available from the British Library.

Typeset in Folio light/medium

Printed in Spain by Gráficas Estella

ISBN 0 19 914693 4

Acknowledgements

The author would like to thank Susan Pople for her help in preparing the manuscript.

The publisher would like to thank the following agencies for their kind permission to reproduce the following photographs:

Allsport / Didier Klein p 145, p 151, / David Cannon p 152, / Bob Martin p 154;
Animal Photography /Sally Anne Thompson p 52; Biophotos Assoc p 73; J Allan Cash p 84, p 96, p 102 (top and bottom), p 162; Bruce Coleman Ltd / Dr Frieder Sauer p 15, / David Davies p 21, / Kim Taylor p 56, / Gerald Cubbit p 58 (bottom right), / Kim Taylor p 58 (bottom left), / Gordon Langsbury p 58 (top left), / Frank Greenaway p 59 (top right), / Kim Taylor p 59 (top left), p 60, / John Murray p 98 (bottom right), / Dieter & Mary Plage p 106, / George McCarthy p 111, / Mr Jens Rydell p 114 (bottom right), / Jane Burton p 172; Daihatsu (UK) Ltd p 160 (left);
G.P.L./ Marijke Heuff p 19 (left), / Jane Legate p 63 (left), / Michael Howes p 103;
S & R Greenhill p 39 (right); G.S.F. Picture Library p 114 (centre right & centre left), / Dr B Booth p 115 (top right and left); Holt Studios Int p 19 (right); Initial Uk Ltd p 161; S & E Marshall & Co p 18; Oxford Scientific Films / Geoff Kidd p 55 (right), / Michael Leach p 71, p 98 (bottom left), / Doug Allen p 114 (bottom left), / Edward Parker p 156 (top left); Samsung Electronics (UK) p 184 (top); Science Photo Library /David Scharf p 34, / Petit Format/Nestle p 36 (top left, middle, right), / Katrina Thomas p 37, / Mark Clarke p 39 (left), / David Scharf p 40 (bottom), / Dr Tony Brain p 44, / Richard Folwell p 66 (bottom left), / Adam Hart-Davis p 67, / Alex Bartel p 92 (right), / Rosenfeld Images Ltd p 100, / European Space Agency p 110, / Sinclair Stammers p 116, / Martin Bond p 117, / Soames Summerhays p 119, / Andrew McClenaghan p 123, / Gordon Garradd p 130, / Heini Schneebeli p 136, / Alex Bartel p 141, / Sheila Terry p 142, / Geoff Tompkinson p 149, / Takeshi Takahara p 153, / Photo Library International p 156 (top right), / Jim Amos p 160 (right), / Johnny Autrey p 169, / Heini Schneebeli p 173, / David Nunuk p 177, / Dr K F R Schiller p 179 (left), / David Parker p 179 (right), / Martin Dohrn p 187 (left), / Gary Parker p 187 (right), / NASA P 190 (Bottom left), / David Parker p 190 (bottom right), / National Snow and Ice Data Services p 190 (top right), / NASA p 191, / Tony Hallas p 194 (bottom right); Tony Stone Worldwide /Tom Tietz p 48 (top), / John Edwards p 63 (right), / David Hiser p 66 (bottom right), p 94, / Tom Tietz p 158, / D Young Riess p 184 (bottom); J Walmsley p 40 (top); Tony Waltham p 114 (top right); Philip Way p 143 (left);

Additional photography by Peter Gould and Martin Sookias.

Cover photograph by Still Pictures.
The illustrations are by: Chris Duggan, Jones Sewell, Pat Murray, Mike Ogden, Oxford Illustrators, Pat Thorne, Borin Van Loon, Pamela Venus and Mike Nicholson

Introduction

If you are working towards GCSE Science (double or single award) Foundation Tier, then this book is for you. It explains the science ideas that you will meet, and helps you find what you need to know. The topics are covered in double-pages which we have called *spreads*.

Contents Here, you can see a list of all the spreads in the book.

Test and check Try answering these questions when you revise. Next to each group of questions, there is a number. This tells you which spread to look up if you need to find out more.

Spread 1.1 This should help you with your investigations.

Spreads 2.1 to 4.38 These are grouped into three sections, matching Attainment Targets 2, 3, and 4 of the National Curriculum.

Extension spreads There are four or five of these at the end of each section. They have a coloured border, and are marked with the symbol ❖ in the contents list. They cover the more advanced ideas you will need if you are aiming for a Grade C in your examination.

Key ideas These are summaries of the main ideas in each section, grouped as in the National Curriculum.

Words and meanings Here, the meanings of the most important scientific words and terms are explained.

GCSE questions These are taken from papers supplied by the GCSE examination boards.

Answers to questions When you have tried the questions, check the answers here.

Index Use this if there are scientific words which you need to look up.

To be a good scientist, you need to carry out investigations. This book should help you understand the scientific ideas behind your investigations. I hope that you will find it useful.

Stephen Pople

Contents

Contents

❖ *This is an extension spread*

Test and check

Can you answer these questions? If not, the spread number tells you where to find out more.

1 Why do animals and plants need food?
2 In what ways are animals and plants the same?
3 What are cells?
4 What are the differences between plant cells and animal cells?

2.1

5 Where is food made in a plant?
6 How does a plant get the energy to make its food?
7 What gas is also made when a plant makes its food?
8 What gas is made when an animal 'burns up' its food?

2.2

9 What is the green chemical in leaves?
10 What does this green chemical do?
11 Where do plants store the food they make?
12 What substance is glucose changed into for storage?
13 In plants, what do hormones do?

2.3

14 In a flower, where are the male cells and where are the female cells?
15 What does 'pollination' mean?
16 Why do some flowers have bright colours?
17 Why do some flowers have stamens that hang out?

2.4

18 How is a flower fertilized?
19 In a flower, what does an ovary become after fertilization?
20 How are seeds scattered?
21 What does 'germination' mean?
22 What does a seed need to germinate?

2.5

23 In your body, how do food, water, and oxygen get to your cells?
24 What job is done by the heart?
25 What job is done by the kidneys?
26 What organ controls the whole body?

2.6

27 Why do you need a skeleton?
28 What job is done by the skull?
29 What is the main mineral in bone?
30 What moves your joints?
31 What do nerves do?

2.7

32 What are the main parts of the gut?
33 What happens to food during digestion?
34 What are enzymes?
35 What happens to food when it has been digested?

2.8

36 How does the heart work?
37 What do arteries do?
38 What do veins do?
39 What are capillaries?
40 Where does blood get rid of carbon dioxide?

2.9

41 What job is done by the lungs?
42 How does oxygen get into your blood?
43 Which way does your diaphragm move when you breathe in?

2.10

44 In a woman, what do the ovaries do?
45 What happens at ovulation?
46 What happens to an egg during fertilization?
47 In a man, where are sperms stored?

2.11

48 In humans, how many months are there between fertilization and birth?
49 Before a baby is born, how does it get its food and oxygen?

2.12

50 What are receptors? Can you give some examples?
51 Where are hormones made? How do they travel round the body?
52 What do hormones do?
53 Why do some people need to take insulin?

2.13

54 What jobs are done by your skin?
55 How can your body cool down if it is too hot?
56 How can your body warm up if it is too cold?

2.14

57 Why do you need proteins in your diet?
58 What foods are rich in vitamin C?
59 What substances give you most of your energy?
60 Why do you need fibre in your diet?

2.15

Test and check

Can you answer these questions? If not, the spread number tells you where to find out more.

1 How many grams are there in a kilogram?
2 What is a measuring cylinder used for? Water has a density of 1000 kg/m³.
3 Can you explain what this means?
4 How is a liquid different from a solid?
5 How is a gas different from a liquid?

3.1

6 What does a liquid become when it evaporates?
7 What is the temperature of boiling water?
8 Why are small gaps left at the ends of bridges?

3.2

9 Can you name a material which is a heat insulator?
10 Can you name a material which is an electrical conductor?
11 Can you list some of the properties of metals?

3.3

12 About how many elements are there?
13 What are the two main types of element?
14 What is the smallest bit of an element called?
15 What is a compound?

3.4

16 What is meant by a 'pure' substance?
17 What is an alloy? Can you give an example of an alloy?
18 What do 'solute', 'solvent', and 'solution' mean?

3.5

19 How would you separate sand from water?
20 How would you separate salt from water?
21 How would you separate inks in a mixture?

3.6

22 If an acid is 'dilute', what does this mean?
23 What effect does an alkali have on an acid?
24 How does an acid affect litmus paper?
25 How does an alkali affect litmus paper?

3.7

26 Can you describe how the particles move in a solid, a liquid, and a gas?
27 If the temperature rises, what happens to the speed of the moving particles?
28 What particles are there in an atom?
29 What is diffusion?

3.8

30 Can you give an example of a chemical change?
31 What are the signs of a chemical change?
32 Can you give an example of a physical change?

3.9

33 How could you show that about 1/5th of the air is oxygen?
34 Can you describe a simple test for oxygen?
35 Can you describe a simple test for carbon-dioxide?
36 What three things are needed for burning?

3.10

37 Can you write a word equation for the reaction between hydrogen and oxygen?
38 When a metal reacts with an acid, what are the products?
39 When a carbonate reacts with an acid, what are the products?

3.11

40 What two things are needed for iron to go rusty?
41 Gold is unreactive. What does this mean?
42 Can you write down some of the useful properties of aluminium?

3.12

43 In a blast furnace, how is iron separated from its ore?
44 Can you name one other element in pig iron, apart from iron?
45 How is steel produced from iron?
46 What are different types of iron and steel used for?

3.13

47 How is limestone formed?
48 What is limestone used for?
49 What is concrete made from?
50 How can soils be made less acid?

3.14

51 What are hydrocarbons?
52 How are the different fractions in crude oil separated?
53 What fuels do we get from oil?
54 What is meant by 'cracking'?
55 What is meant by 'polymerization'?
56 Can you give some examples of products made from oil?

3.15

57 What are the two main gases in air? Which of these gases is there most of? Which of these gases do animals and plants need to stay alive?
58 Can you name any other gases in air? Can you describe some uses of these gases?

3.16

59 Why do farmers add fertilizers to the soil?
60 What reaction is used to make ammonia?
61 How is Nitram fertilizer made?
62 What problems are caused by putting too much fertilizer on the soil?

3.17

63 Can you explain how water in the sea can end up coming out of your tap?
64 At what temperature does water freeze?
65 What damage can water cause when it freezes?

3.18

66 What happens to a rock during weathering?
67 Can you give three causes of weathering?
68 What is erosion?
69 Can you explain how bits from one rock can end up forming new rock?

3.19

70 How are igneous rocks formed?
71 How are sedimentary rocks formed?
72 How are metamorphic rocks formed?
73 Can you give examples of an igneous rock, a sedimentary rock, and a metamorphic rock?

3.20

74 What are strata? How are they formed?
75 Where are the oldest rock layers usually found?
76 Why are there no fossils is igneous rocks?
77 What causes folds in rocks?

3.21

78 What is the Earth's core like?
79 Where is the mantle?
80 Why do the continents seem to fit together like pieces of jigsaw?
81 What are plates?
82 Where do earthquakes and volcanoes mainly happen?

3.22

Extension spreads

83 How are the electrons arranged in an atom?
84 Why is sodium very reactive?
85 Why is helium unreactive?
86 What are isotopes?
87 What are ions?
88 How are atoms held to each other?

3.23

89 In the periodic table, what do elements in the same group have in common?
90 Can you name some transition metals?
91 Can you describe some properties of the alkali metals?
92 Can you describe some properties of the halogens?

3.24

93 When an acid reacts with a base, what are the products?
94 What is the pH of a neutral solution?
95 If a solution has a pH of 10, is it an acid or an alkali?
96 What is the reactivity series?
97 What useful substances can be produced from salt?

3.25

98 What is an exothermic reaction?
99 Can you give an example of a reversible reaction?
100 What happens in a precipitation reaction?
101 What does the rate of a chemical reaction depend on?
102 What is a catalyst?

3.26

103 How has the Earth's atmosphere changed since it was formed?
104 What is the difference between intrusive and extrusive igneous rock?
105 If an igneous rock has small crystals, what does this tell you about it?
106 What is magma?
107 What is the rock cycle?

3.27

Test and check

Can you answer these questions? If not, the spread number tells you where to find out more.

1 What materials conduct electricity?
2 What types of charge repel?
3 What types of charge attract?
4 What materials are good electrical insulators?

4.1

5 Can you draw a circuit with a bulb, battery, and switch in it? Can you add meters to measure the voltage across the battery, and the current?

4.2

6 Can you draw a circuit with a battery and two bulbs in series?
7 Can you draw a circuit with a battery and two bulbs in parallel?

4.3

8 How would you use a variable resistor to vary the brightness of a bulb?
9 What is inside a heating element?
10 In what units is power measured?

4.4

11 Can you draw the magnetic field round a bar magnet?
12 How is an electromagnet made?
13 Can you explain how a relay works?

4.5

14 What happens when you move a magnet in or out of a coil?
15 What is 'AC'?
16 How does an AC generator work?
17 How is mains power sent across country?

4.6

18 What is the mains frequency in Britain?
19 In a three-pin plug, what colours are used for the live, neutral, and earth wires?
20 How can you decide which is the correct fuse to use in a plug?

4.7

21 What is a newtonmeter used for?
22 In what units is force measured?
23 Can you give an example of balanced forces?

4.8

24 When you push in a drawing pin, is the pressure greatest under your thumb, or under the point? Can you explain why?

4.9

25 What happens to the pressure as you go deeper into water?
26 What is an upthrust?
27 How do hydraulic machines work?

4.10

28 How can you get a stronger turning effect from a spanner?
29 What is a 'centre of gravity'?

4.11

30 Can you explain what a 'speed of 10 metres per second' means?
31 Can you give some examples of friction being useful?

4.12

32 In what units is energy measured?
33 Can you give some examples of different forms of energy?
34 What is the law of conservation of energy?

4.13

35 Can you think of something which has a high temperature but does not store much heat?
36 Can you give an example of something that stores energy?

4.14

37 Which materials are good conductors of heat?
38 Which materials are good insulators?
39 What is a convection current?
40 How is convection used to heat a room?

4.15

41 Which surfaces are best at absorbing heat radiation?
42 Which surfaces radiate heat most slowly?
43 Why do wet hands feel cold when you put them in a draught?

4.16

44 Can you describe how a fuel-burning power station works?
45 How does a hydroelectric power station work?

4.17

46 What are fossil fuels?
47 Can you give some examples of renewable energy supplies?
48 Where does the energy in your food come from?

4.18

49 Can you explain how most of the world's energy comes from the Sun? **4.19**

50 What are 'sound waves'?
51 How are sounds made?
52 Why do you see lightning before you hear it? **4.20**

53 Can you describe how the ear works?
54 If a guitar string vibrates faster, how does this affect the sound? How do bigger vibrations affect the sound? **4.21**

55 What is the speed of sound in air?
56 What causes echoes?
57 How does echo sounding work?
58 What is ultrasound used for? **4.22**

59 How are shadows formed?
60 Can you draw a diagram showing how a ray of light reflects from a mirror?
61 If you put something in front of a flat mirror, where is the image seen? **4.23**

62 What does 'refraction' mean?
63 What happens to a ray of light when it goes into a glass block? **4.24**

64 How can a prism be used to reflect light?
65 What is meant by the 'critical angle'?
66 How does an optical fibre work?
67 What are optical fibres used for? **4.25**

68 What is the difference between a convex lens and a concave lens?
69 How is an image formed in a camera?
70 How is an image formed in the eye? **4.26**

71 How would you produce a spectrum?
72 How could you make white using three beams of coloured light?
73 Why does a red book look red? **4.27**

74 What are the different types of electromagnetic radiation?
75 Can you put these different types in order of wavelength? **4.28**

76 Can you name three types of nuclear radiation?
77 How can nuclear radiation be detected?
78 Which type of nuclear radiation is the most penetrating? **4.29**

79 Why do we get day and night?
80 How long does the Earth take to go round the Sun?
81 Why do we have seasons? **4.30**

82 How long does the Moon take to go round the Earth?
83 Can you describe some of the jobs that satellites are used for? **4.31**

84 Can you describe how the planets move round the Sun?
85 Can you list the planets in order, starting with the one nearest the Sun? **4.32**

86 What is measured in light years?
87 What is a galaxy?
88 What is a nebula?
89 How are stars formed? **4.33**

Extension spreads

90 What equation links resistance, voltage, and current?
91 In what units is resistance measured?
92 What equation links power, voltage, and current?
93 What is a diode? **4.34**

94 How could you get a stronger field from an electromagnet?
95 How does a simple DC motor work?
96 How does a circuit breaker work?
97 What does a transformer do? **4.35**

98 How do you calculate speed?
99 How do you calculate acceleration? What is a moment?
100 How do you calculate pressure? What is Hooke's law? **4.36**

101 How do you calculate work done?
102 What equation links power, work done, and time?
103 If an engine has an efficiency of 25%, what does this mean?
104 How do you calculate the cost of using mains electricity? **4.37**

105 What is the difference between a longitudinal and a transverse wave?
106 What is meant by the amplitude of a wave?
107 What types of radiation are ionizing? **4.38**

1.1 Doing an investigation

Here is an investigation:

Find out if sugar dissolves more quickly in hot water than in cold

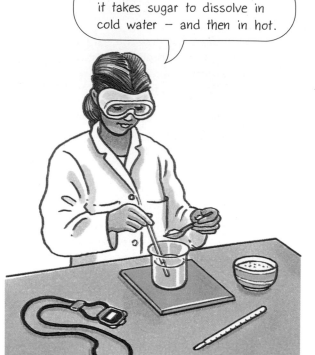

I'm going to measure the time it takes sugar to dissolve in cold water – and then in hot.

You could do this like the girl on the right. But first, you need to know about the following:

▶ Key factors

In any investigation, you must decide what the **key factors** are. These are the things which affect what happens. In this investigation, the key factors are:

type of sugar
amount of sugar
amount of water
whether you stir or not
temperature of water
time for sugar to dissolve

▶ A fair test?

In the investigation, you must make sure that each test is fair.

For a fair test, you change just one factor (the temperature) and see how this affects one other factor (the time to dissolve):

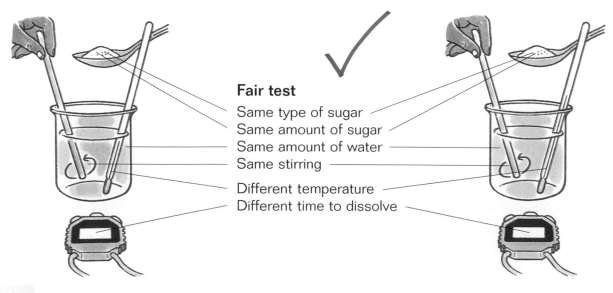

Fair test
Same type of sugar
Same amount of sugar
Same amount of water
Same stirring

Different temperature
Different time to dissolve

The test below is not a fair one. Lots of factors change as well as the temperature. So you cannot tell what effect the temperature is having:

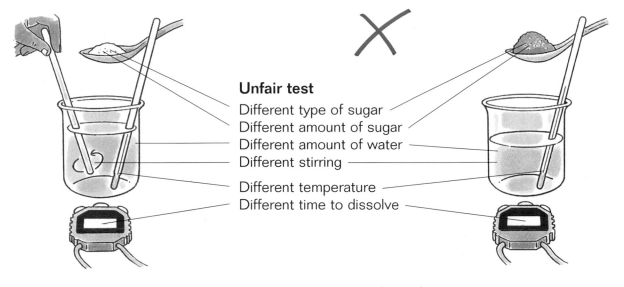

Unfair test
Different type of sugar
Different amount of sugar
Different amount of water
Different stirring
Different temperature
Different time to dissolve

▷ **Table.....**

When you take readings, write them down in a table like this:

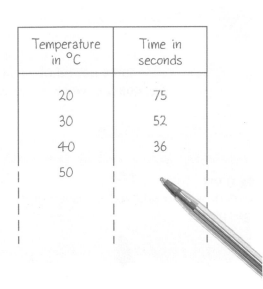

Temperature in °C	Time in seconds
20	75
30	52
40	36
50	

.....and graph

If you have several sets of readings, plot a graph. It will show you if the readings follow a pattern:

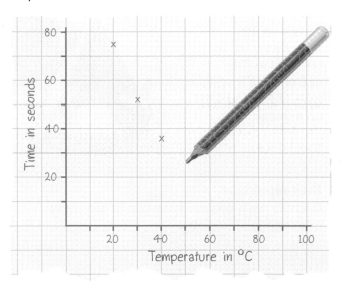

▷ **Conclusion**

Your **conclusion** is what you found out. For example, from the points on the graph, your conclusion might be this:

The hotter the water, the less time it takes the sugar to dissolve

2.1 Looking at life

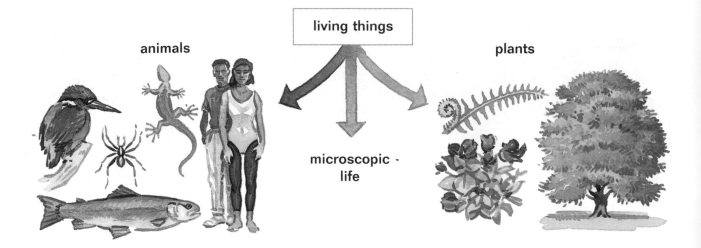

animals

living things

plants

microscopic - life

Animals and plants are living things. This is what living things are like:

They need food
It gives them energy.

They use air
They use it to 'burn up' food in their bodies. It is a special type of burning with no flames.

Their bodies make waste
You breathe out waste gas and go to the toilet. Plants get rid of waste gas and water.

They reproduce
Animals have babies. New plants can grow from seeds.

They grow
Babies grow into adults. Seedlings grow into bigger plants.

They react
Animals react to light and noise. Plants grow towards the light.

They move
Animals move most. But even plants move a little.

► Made from cells

Living things are made from tiny bits called **cells**.
Your body is made from millions of cells.

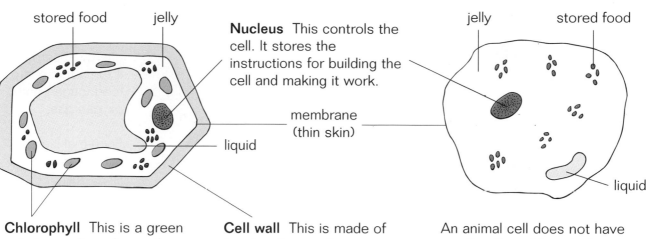

Plant cell

stored food   jelly

Nucleus This controls the cell. It stores the instructions for building the cell and making it work.

membrane (thin skin)

liquid

Animal cell

jelly   stored food

liquid

Chlorophyll This is a green substance. It soaks up the energy in the Sun's rays.

Cell wall This is made of tough cellulose. It makes stems and branches strong.

An animal cell does not have a cell wall or chlorophyll.

1 *cells   animals   body   plants   nucleus*
   Copy the sentences below. Fill in the blanks, choosing words from those above:
      Animals and _____ are living things.
      Living things are made from _____.
      There are millions of cells in your _____.
      A cell is controlled by its _____.

2 Write down *one* example of each of these:
   a An animal getting energy.
   b A plant reproducing.
   c An animal reacting.
   d A plant reacting.

3 Copy the diagrams below. Write in these labels:
   animal   plant   nucleus   cell wall

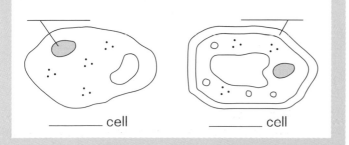

_____ cell   _____ cell

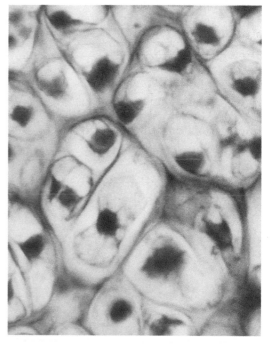

Human cheek cells, magnified 1500 times

15

Making and using food

Animals have to find their food. But plants make their own.

A plant takes carbon dioxide gas from the air, and water from the soil.....

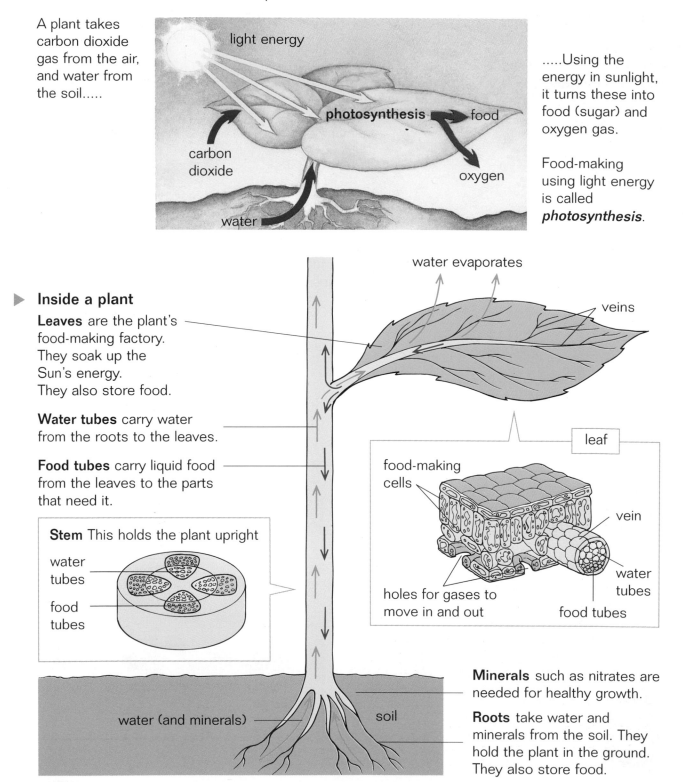

.....Using the energy in sunlight, it turns these into food (sugar) and oxygen gas.

Food-making using light energy is called **photosynthesis**.

▶ **Inside a plant**

Leaves are the plant's food-making factory. They soak up the Sun's energy. They also store food.

Water tubes carry water from the roots to the leaves.

Food tubes carry liquid food from the leaves to the parts that need it.

Stem This holds the plant upright

water tubes

food tubes

Minerals such as nitrates are needed for healthy growth.

Roots take water and minerals from the soil. They hold the plant in the ground. They also store food.

▶ Burning up food

Plants make and store food. Animals can get this food by eating plants. That is why you eat fruit and vegetables.

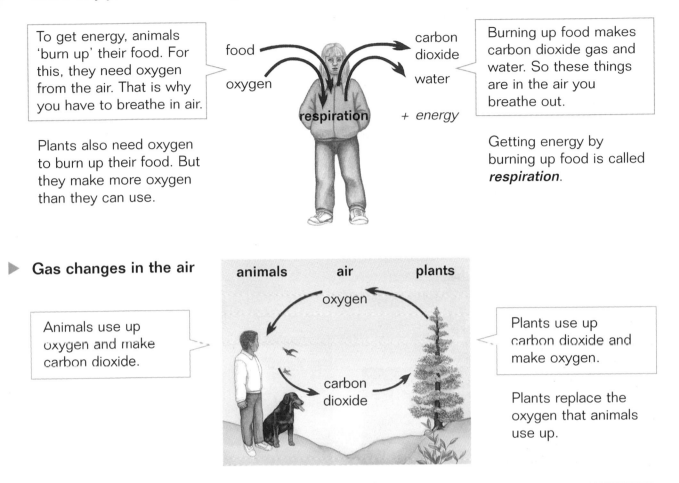

To get energy, animals 'burn up' their food. For this, they need oxygen from the air. That is why you have to breathe in air.

Plants also need oxygen to burn up their food. But they make more oxygen than they can use.

food → ← oxygen → respiration → carbon dioxide → water + energy

Burning up food makes carbon dioxide gas and water. So these things are in the air you breathe out.

Getting energy by burning up food is called *respiration*.

▶ Gas changes in the air

animals   air   plants

oxygen

carbon dioxide

Animals use up oxygen and make carbon dioxide.

Plants use up carbon dioxide and make oxygen.

Plants replace the oxygen that animals use up.

1 Copy the diagram on the right.
  Shade in the parts where the plant makes its food.
  Label them 'Food is made here'.

2 *sunlight   oxygen   carbon dioxide   leaves*
  Copy the sentences below. Fill in the blanks, choosing words from those above. (You may use the same word more than once.)
     To make their food, plants use the energy in ____.
     Plants take in ____ gas and give out ____ gas.
     Animals take in ____ gas and give out ____ gas.
     To burn up their food, animals need ____.

3 Describe how water gets to the leaves of a plant.

4 Describe how a plant gets the minerals it needs.

5 Describe how gases get in and out of a leaf.

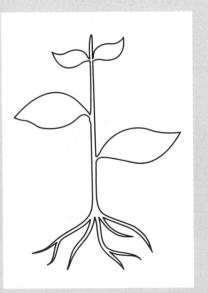

Plants at work

▶ Making and storing food

Plants need food for energy and growth. Their main food is a type of sugar called *glucose*. They make it from carbon dioxide and water, using the energy in sunlight.

Glucose dissolves in water. It travels through the plant in its food tubes.

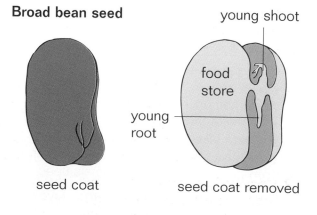

leaf

glucose made

starch stored

To soak up the energy in sunlight, plants have a green chemical called chlorophyll in their leaves. That is why they are green.

starch stored

When plants make glucose, they do not need it all straightaway. So they change some of it into *starch*. This is stored in their leaves and roots. Later, when they need its energy, the starch is changed back into glucose.

Starch is stored in the bulging parts of these carrots. We get energy by eating them.

Broad bean seed

young shoot

food store

young root

seed coat

seed coat removed

Seeds have food stored in them. It keeps them going until the tiny shoot comes out. Then the seedling (new plant) can make its own food.

▶ Hormones in control

Plants have chemicals called **hormones** in them. Hormones control how different parts of the plant grow. They travel through the plant with the liquid in its food tubes.

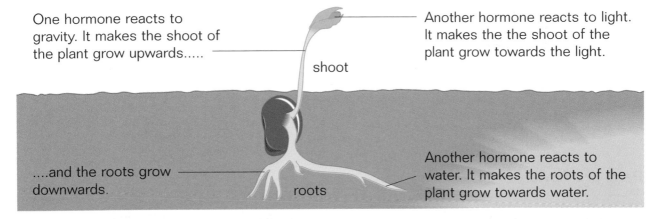

One hormone reacts to gravity. It makes the shoot of the plant grow upwards.....

Another hormone reacts to light. It makes the the shoot of the plant grow towards the light.

shoot

....and the roots grow downwards.

roots

Another hormone reacts to water. It makes the roots of the plant grow towards water.

▶ Using plant hormones

Gardeners sometimes dip their cuttings in hormone powder. This makes new roots grow more quickly.

Some weedkillers have a hormone in. It makes the weeds grow too quickly so that they run out of food and energy, and die.

1 Choose the word on the right which goes with each of these:
   a Type of sugar, made in the leaves of a plant.
   b Plants change glucose into this for storage.
   c Plants use its energy to make their food.
   d Chemical which controls how a plant grows.

2 Copy and complete these sentences:
   Leaves are green because....
   Shoots grow upwards, and towards....
   Roots grow downwards, and towards....
   Cuttings are dipped in hormone powder because....

starch

glucose

hormone

light

soil

Flowers

New plants grow from seeds.
Seeds come from flowers.

Flowers have **sex cells** inside them. To make a
seed, a **male cell** must join with a **female cell**.

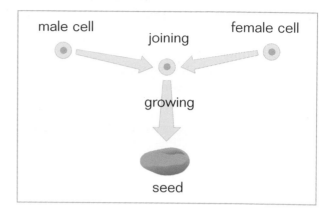

▶ Parts of a flower

Stamen This has a bulge at the end
called an **anther**. It holds thousands of
tiny grains of **pollen**. There is a male cell
in each grain.

When the **anther** splits open, the pollen
grains fall out.

pollen grains
with male cells

Carpel This has an **ovary** inside, where
tiny eggs grow. The eggs are called
ovules. There is a female cell in each one.

The carpel has a sticky end called a
stigma. Pollen can stick to this.

ovary

ovule

stigma

female cell

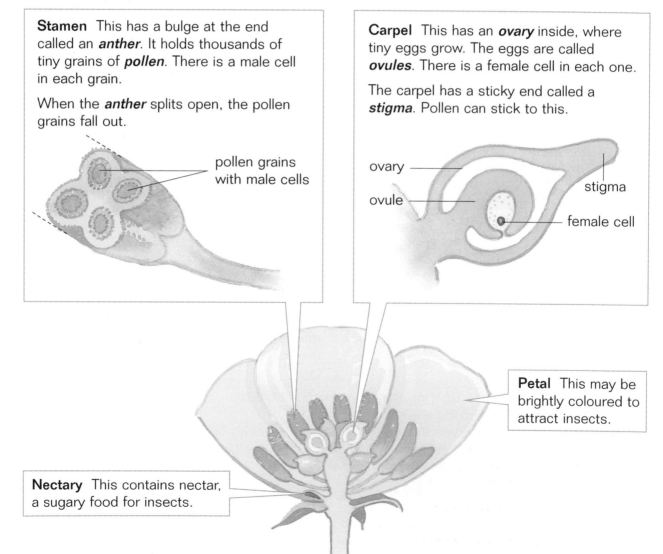

Petal This may be
brightly coloured to
attract insects.

Nectary This contains nectar,
a sugary food for insects.

▶ Pollinating flowers

Before a male cell can join with a female cell, pollen must get across to a stigma and stick to it. This is called **pollination**. Usually, the pollen is carried across to another flower.

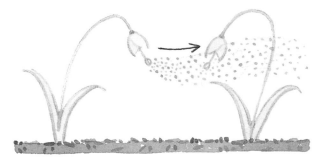

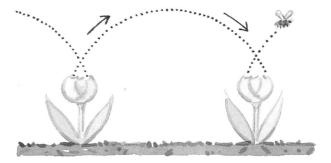

Some flowers are pollinated by wind Their flowers have stamens that hang out in the wind. When their pollen is blown away, some lands on other flowers.

Some flowers are pollinated by insects The insects are attracted by the scent or bright colours. As they search for nectar, they get covered in pollen and carry it to other flowers.

After pollination, the male and female sex cells can join. To find out how, see the next page.

1 *pollen   ovules   nectar   petal*

Copy the diagram below. Fill in the blanks, choosing words from those above:

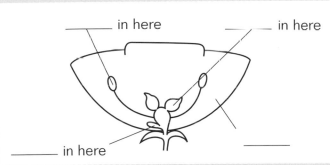

2 *pollination   male   female   flowering*

Copy the sentences below. Fill in the blanks, choosing words from those above:

In each ovule, there is a ____ cell.
In each pollen grain, there is a ____ cell.
When pollen sticks to a stigma, this is called ____.

3 Look at the photograph on the right.
  a Explain why the flower is brightly coloured.
  b Explain what the bee is doing.
  c Explain how a bee pollinates flowers.

Fruits and seeds

▶ Fertilization

After pollination, when pollen grains stick to a stigma, this is what happens:

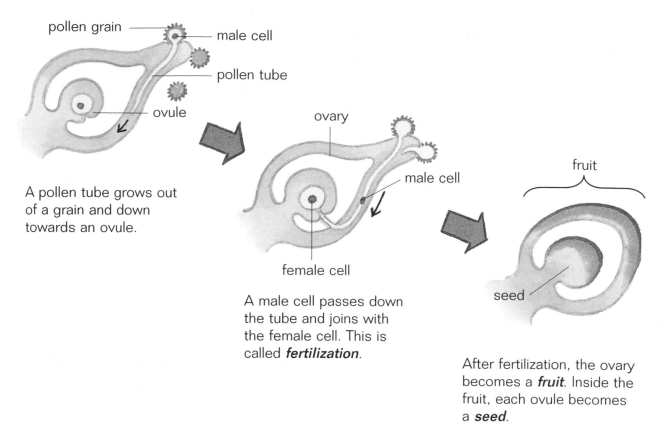

A pollen tube grows out of a grain and down towards an ovule.

A male cell passes down the tube and joins with the female cell. This is called *fertilization*.

After fertilization, the ovary becomes a *fruit*. Inside the fruit, each ovule becomes a *seed*.

▶ Scattering seeds

Flowers try to scatter their seeds over a wide area. This is so that more may survive and grow into new plants. The scattering of seeds is called *dispersal*.

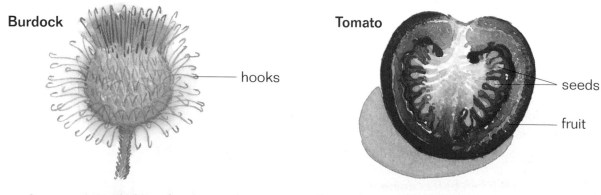

Some fruits and seeds have hooks so that they are carried by animals.

Some fruits are eaten by animals. The seeds come out with their droppings.

Sycamore

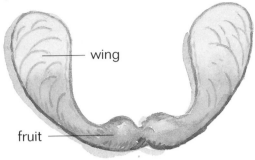

wing

fruit

Some fruits and seeds are shaped so that they can be carried by the wind.

Pea

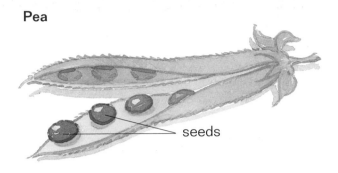

seeds

Some seeds are in pods. When dry, these pop open and flick out the seeds.

▶ **Germination**

A seed has a store of food inside it.

When a seed starts to grow, this is called *germination*.

To germinate, a seed needs.....

water	warmth	air

When a seed germinates:
A tiny *shoot* grows upwards towards the light.
A tiny *root* grows downwards into the soil.

Germination of a broad bean

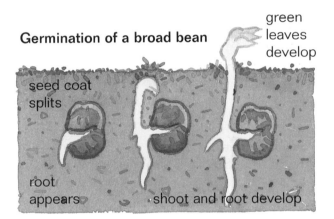

green leaves develop

seed coat splits

root appears

shoot and root develop

---

1 *germination*   *fertilization*   *scattering*

Copy the sentences below. Fill in the blanks, choosing words from those above:
   A male cell joining with a female cell is called ____.
   A seed starting to grow is called ____.

2 Copy these sentences in the correct order:
   A male cell joins with a female cell.
   Pollen sticks to a stigma.
   A male cell passes down the pollen tube.
   The ovule becomes a seed.
   Pollen is carried from one flower to another.
   A pollen tube grows down towards an ovule.

3 Write down *three* things which seeds need to germinate.

4 Look at the diagram on the right.
   Describe how you think the seeds are scattered.

Dandelion

fruit

Organs of the body

An **organ** is any part of the body with a special job to do. The next page shows some of the main organs of the human body. The organs are all made of tiny cells.

▶ **The body at work**

Your body takes in food, water, and oxygen. The blood carries them to all your organs. There, the cells use them for growth and for getting energy.

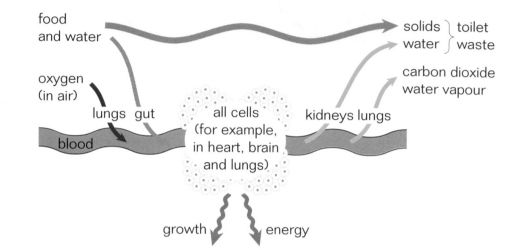

food and water

oxygen (in air)

lungs gut

blood

all cells (for example, in heart, brain and lungs)

kidneys lungs

solids ⎫ toilet
water ⎰ waste

carbon dioxide water vapour

growth   energy

Your body gives out waste. Some is unused food that goes right through you. But cells also make waste, such as carbon dioxide and water. The blood carries these to the organs that get rid of them:

The **kidneys** get rid of water (through your bladder).

The **lungs** get rid of carbon dioxide and water (as damp air).

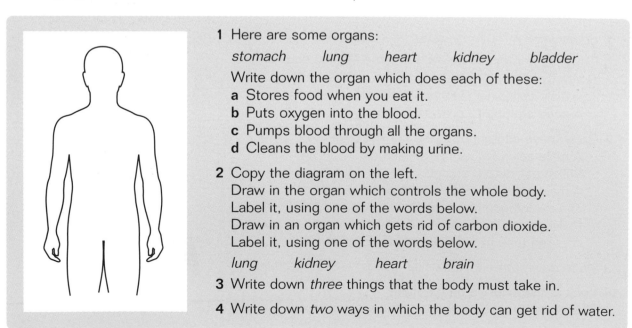

1 Here are some organs:

   stomach   lung   heart   kidney   bladder

  Write down the organ which does each of these:
  a Stores food when you eat it.
  b Puts oxygen into the blood.
  c Pumps blood through all the organs.
  d Cleans the blood by making urine.

2 Copy the diagram on the left.
  Draw in the organ which controls the whole body.
  Label it, using one of the words below.
  Draw in an organ which gets rid of carbon dioxide.
  Label it, using one of the words below.

   lung   kidney   heart   brain

3 Write down *three* things that the body must take in.

4 Write down *two* ways in which the body can get rid of water.

Brain controls the whole body.

Eyes form pictures of the outside world. They send signals to the brain.

Ears pick up sounds and send signals to the brain.

Lungs take oxygen from the air into the blood. They also get rid of carbon dioxide (and some water).

Heart pumps blood through all your organs.

Liver is a 'chemical factory' which deals with useful things in the blood and stores some of them.

Stomach is part of the gut. It stores the food you eat while chemicals get to work on it.

Gut is a long tube where food is dealt with so that useful things can get into the blood.

Kidneys clean the blood. They make a waste liquid called urine. This is mainly water.

Bladder stores urine until you go to the toilet.

Muscles move your arms and legs.

Bones, joints, and muscles

▶ **The skeleton**

Your body is held up by a **skeleton**. This has several jobs to do:

Support The skeleton lets you stand upright. It also supports organs inside you.

Protection The skeleton protects many organs.

Movement The skeleton has joints so that you can move bits of your body. The joints are moved by muscles.

teeth for cutting

teeth for crushing

teeth for gripping

Teeth Adults have 32 of these.

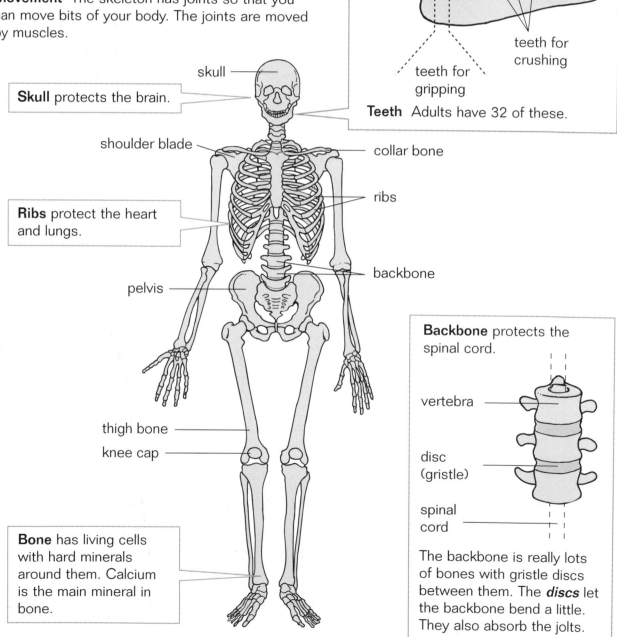

skull

Skull protects the brain.

shoulder blade

collar bone

ribs

Ribs protect the heart and lungs.

backbone

pelvis

Backbone protects the spinal cord.

vertebra

disc (gristle)

spinal cord

thigh bone

knee cap

Bone has living cells with hard minerals around them. Calcium is the main mineral in bone.

The backbone is really lots of bones with gristle discs between them. The **discs** let the backbone bend a little. They also absorb the jolts.

Joints and muscles

To bend a joint, a muscle contracts (gets shorter). But it cannot get longer again by itself. So muscles are arranged in pairs.
One muscle pulls the joint one way, the other pulls it back again.

Raising arm

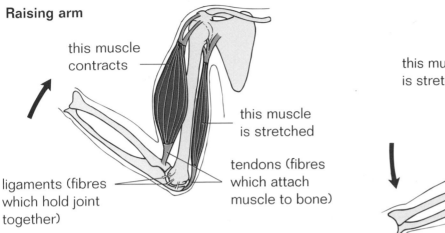

this muscle contracts

this muscle is stretched

ligaments (fibres which hold joint together)

tendons (fibres which attach muscle to bone)

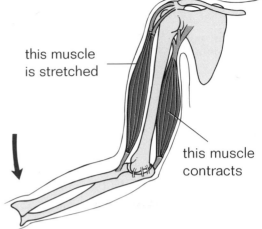

this muscle is stretched

this muscle contracts

Nerves

To control your muscles, signals are sent along *nerves*.

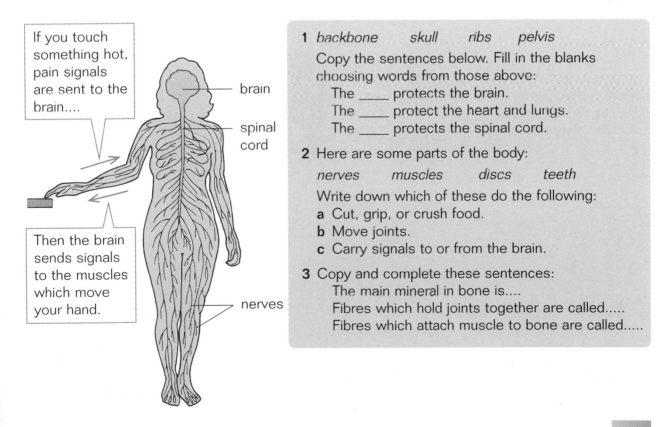

If you touch something hot, pain signals are sent to the brain....

brain

spinal cord

Then the brain sends signals to the muscles which move your hand.

nerves

1 *backbone   skull   ribs   pelvis*
  Copy the sentences below. Fill in the blanks choosing words from those above:
      The ____ protects the brain.
      The ____ protect the heart and lungs.
      The ____ protects the spinal cord.

2 Here are some parts of the body:
  nerves   muscles   discs   teeth
  Write down which of these do the following:
  a Cut, grip, or crush food.
  b Move joints.
  c Carry signals to or from the brain.

3 Copy and complete these sentences:
      The main mineral in bone is....
      Fibres which hold joints together are called.....
      Fibres which attach muscle to bone are called.....

27

Dealing with food

▶ The gut

This is a long tube that runs from your mouth down through your body. This is where food is dealt with.

The main parts of the gut are:

mouth, gullet, stomach, small intestine, large intestine.

When you eat, the useful things in your food must get into your blood. But first, they must be changed into a liquid. This is called *digestion*.

In your gut, there are special chemicals for digesting food. These are called *enzymes*.

Your gut is over 6 metres long.

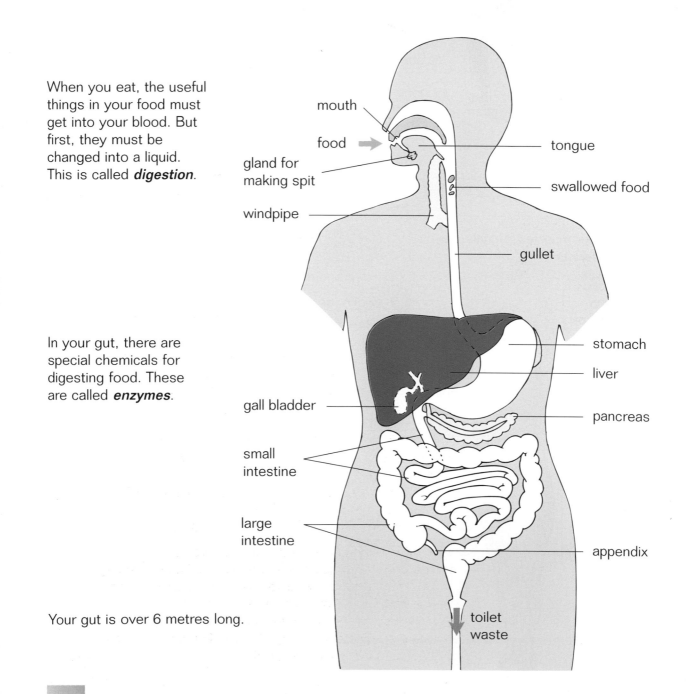

mouth

food

gland for making spit

windpipe

tongue

swallowed food

gullet

stomach

liver

pancreas

gall bladder

small intestine

large intestine

appendix

toilet waste

▶ What happens to your food

Digestion
Digestion starts in your mouth. When you chew, food gets mixed with spit. The spit has an enzyme in it. This changes solid bits of starch into liquid sugar.

Enzymes turn food into liquid. This mainly happens in the stomach and small intestine.

Absorption
Digested food (liquid) seeps into the blood. This mainly happens in the small intestine.

In the large intestine, most of the water in undigested matter is absorbed by the blood.

food into mouth

gullet

stomach

In your stomach, food is mixed with juice. The juice has acid and an enzyme in it.

small intestine

large intestine

Undigested matter is pushed out of your body when you go to the toilet.

---

1 *absorption   digestion   enzymes   blood*
   Copy the sentences below. Fill in the blanks, choosing words from those above.
   The useful things in your food must get into your ____.
   Changing solid food into liquid is called ____.
   Your food is digested by chemicals called ____.

2 Copy these sentences in the correct order:
   In the stomach, food is mixed with acid and an enzyme.
   Undigested food passes through the large intestine.
   Food is chewed and mixed with spit.
   Undigested food goes down the toilet.
   In the small intestine, digested food seeps into the blood.
   Food passes down the gullet.

2.9 Blood and the heart

▶ Jobs done by the blood

- Bringing oxygen, water, and food to cells all round the body.
- Taking away carbon dioxide and other waste from the cells.
- Carrying heat round the body.
- Carrying **hormones**. These are chemicals which control how different organs work.
- Carrying things which fight germs.

▶ Blood

Blood is a mixture of things. This is what it would look like through a powerful microscope.

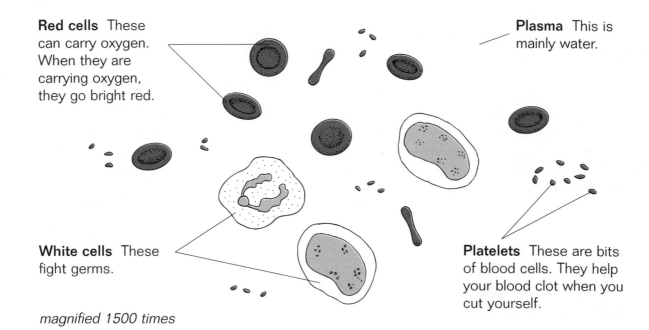

Red cells These can carry oxygen. When they are carrying oxygen, they go bright red.

Plasma This is mainly water.

White cells These fight germs.

Platelets These are bits of blood cells. They help your blood clot when you cut yourself.

magnified 1500 times

▶ Circulating blood

The heart pumps blood round the body through tubes called arteries, capillaries, and veins:

Arteries These carry blood away from the heart.

Capillaries These are thousands of narrow tubes running from arteries to veins. Every cell in the body is close to a capillary so that blood can bring the cell the things it needs.

Veins These carry blood back to the heart. Some have valves in so that blood can only flow one way.

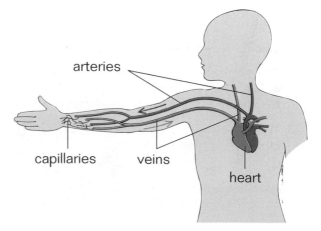

arteries

capillaries   veins

heart

▶ The heart

The heart is really two pumps side by side. One pump sends blood to the lungs, to collect oxygen. The other takes blood from the lungs and pumps it round the rest of the body.

blood collects oxygen

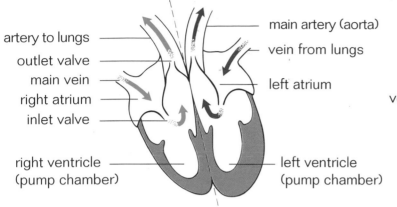

artery

vein

lung capillaries

artery to lungs
outlet valve
main vein
right atrium
inlet valve

main artery (aorta)
vein from lungs
left atrium

right ventricle
(pump chamber)

left ventricle
(pump chamber)

vein

heart
(two pumps)

artery

body capillaries

Each pump has two **valves** and a chamber called a **ventricle**. When your heart **beats**, the chamber gets bigger, smaller, bigger, smaller.... and so on. This pulls in blood through one valve and pushes it out through the other.

blood delivers oxygen

1 *white   red   plasma*
  Copy these sentences. Fill in the blanks, choosing words from those above:
  ____ blood cells fight germs.
  ____ blood cells can carry oxygen.

2 Here are three types of blood tube:
  vein   capillary   artery
  Write down which type does each of these:
  a Carries blood away from the heart.
  b Carries blood back to the heart.

3 The diagram on the right shows how blood circulates round the body.
  Copy the diagram. Then write in these labels:
  heart   oxygen collected here   oxygen delivered here

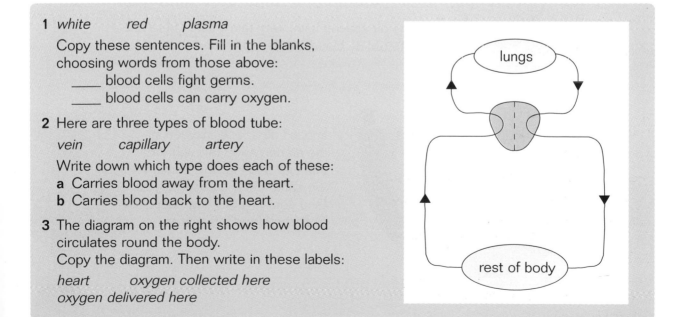

lungs

rest of body

The lungs and breathing

▶ The lungs

The cells of your body use up oxygen. At the same time, they make carbon dioxide (and water) which they do not want. The job of the lungs is to put oxygen into the blood, and remove carbon dioxide (and some water).

The lungs are two spongy bags. They are filled with millions of tiny air spaces.

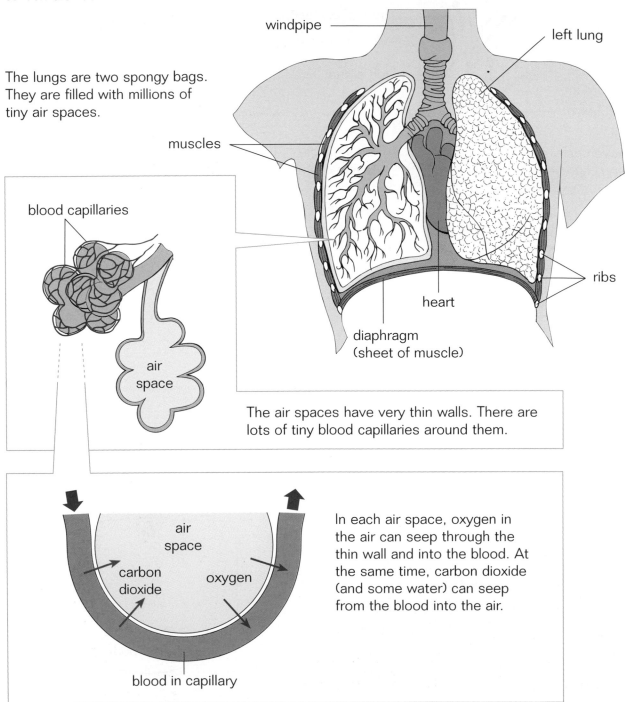

The air spaces have very thin walls. There are lots of tiny blood capillaries around them.

In each air space, oxygen in the air can seep through the thin wall and into the blood. At the same time, carbon dioxide (and some water) can seep from the blood into the air.

▶ Breathing

As you breathe in and out, your lungs get bigger and smaller.
Some of the old air in your lungs is replaced by new. There is
an *exchange* of carbon dioxide and oxygen.

Breathing in

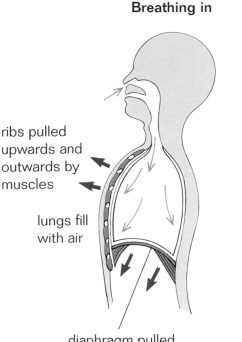

ribs pulled
upwards and
outwards by
muscles

lungs fill
with air

diaphragm pulled
downwards by muscles

Breathing out

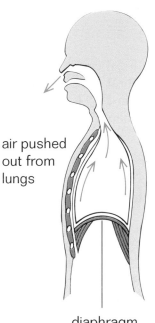

air pushed
out from
lungs

diaphragm
relaxes

If you are running, you burn up food faster. So you must take
in more oxygen and get rid of more carbon dioxide. That is why
you have to breathe faster.

1 *rib   lung   heart   diaphragm   windpipe*
   Copy the diagram on the right. Fill in the blanks using the
   labels above.

2 *diaphragm   air   water   blood   lungs   ribs*
   Copy these sentences. Fill in the blanks, choosing words
   from those above:
   When you breathe in, your ____ move upwards and
   outwards, your ____ moves downwards, and your
   ____ fill with ____. In your lungs, the tiny air spaces
   are surrounded by ____ capillaries.

3 In your lungs, what gas goes into the blood?

4 In your lungs, what gas comes out of the blood?

5 Explain why you breathe faster when you are running.

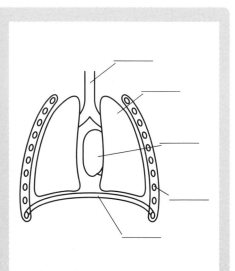

Making human life

A baby grows from a tiny cell in its mother. The cell is made when a tiny egg, or *ovum*, inside the mother is fertilized by a *sperm* from the father.

▶ Puberty

This is the time when a girl can first become a mother, and a boy can first become a father. For girls, the age is often 12-14. For boys it is often 14-16. But later than this is quite normal.

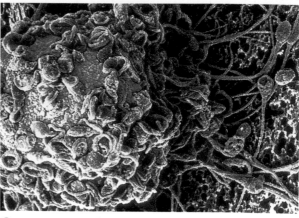

Sperms around an egg, magnified 1000 times

▶ A woman's sex system

Ovulation About every 28 days, a woman releases an egg from one of her *ovaries*. This is called *ovulation*. The tiny egg moves down the *egg tube* and into the *uterus* (womb).

Lining growth The lining of the womb thickens, and blood capillaries grow in it. The womb is now ready for a fertilized egg.

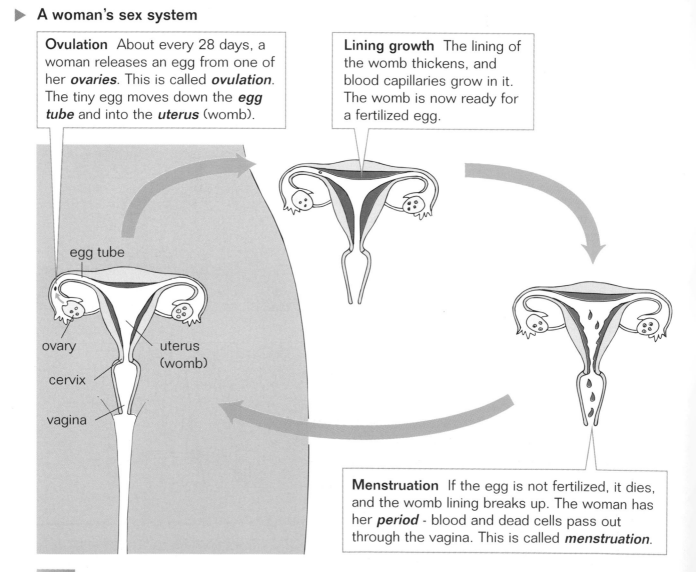

egg tube

ovary

uterus (womb)

cervix

vagina

Menstruation If the egg is not fertilized, it dies, and the womb lining breaks up. The woman has her *period* - blood and dead cells pass out through the vagina. This is called *menstruation*.

A man's sex system

A man makes sperms in his **testicles**.

Before sperms leave his body, they are mixed with a liquid. Sperms and liquid are called **semen**. Semen comes out of the man's penis.

Fertilization

When a man and woman have sex, the man's penis goes stiff and is put in the woman's vagina. Then semen shoots out of his penis. There are millions of sperms, but only one can fertilize the egg.

bladder

sperm duct

glands make liquid for semen

penis

testicles: sperms are made here

blood pressure in this tissue stiffens penis

Birth control

Parents may want a small family. If so, they may decide to use **contraception** (birth control). Here are some of the methods:

Condom This is a rubber cover which fits over the man's penis. It traps sperms. It is only reliable if used with a cream which kills sperms.

The pill The woman takes this every day. It stops her ovaries releasing eggs. It is reliable, but can cause heart, liver, and breast disease.

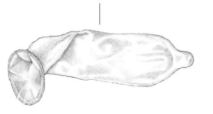

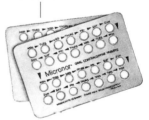

Diaphragm This is a rubber cover which fits over the woman's cervix. It stops sperms reaching the womb. It is only reliable if used with a cream which kills sperms.

Natural method The woman does tests to find out when ovulation is close, and does not have sex near that time. This method can be used by people who think that other kinds of birth control are wrong.

1 Copy these sentences in the correct order, starting with the one which tells you about *ovulation*:
   The woman has her period.
   If the egg is not fertilized, the womb lining breaks up.
   An ovary releases an egg, and the womb lining thickens.

2 *ovaries   testicles   fertilization   menstruation*
   From the above words, choose one for each of these:
   a Sperms are made in these.
   b Eggs are released from these.
   c A sperm joining with an egg.

Growing to be born

Actual sizes

Fertilized egg

Embryo

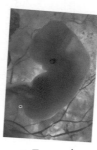

...at 4 weeks

...at 7 weeks

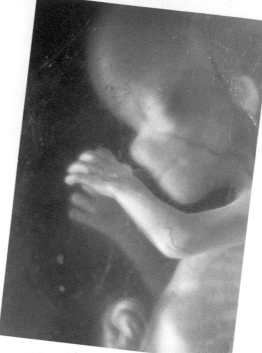

▶ From egg to embryo

If a human egg is fertilized, it grows into a tiny ball of cells. This is called an **embryo**. It sinks into the lining of the womb and starts to grow into a baby.

▶ The growing embryo

After six weeks, the embryo has a heart and a brain. It lies in a bag of watery liquid which protects it from jolts and bumps.

...at 14 weeks

The embryo cannot eat or breath, so it must get all the things it needs from its mother's blood. It does this through an organ called the **placenta**. This grows into the womb lining.

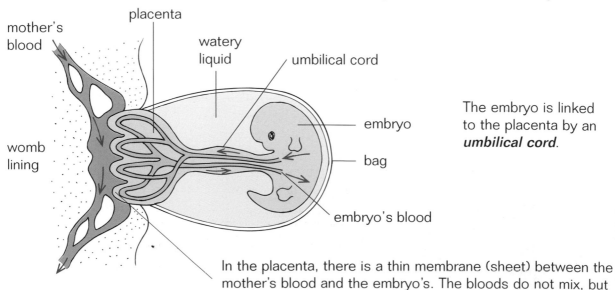

mother's blood

placenta

watery liquid

umbilical cord

womb lining

embryo

bag

embryo's blood

The embryo is linked to the placenta by an **umbilical cord**.

In the placenta, there is a thin membrane (sheet) between the mother's blood and the embryo's. The bloods do not mix, but food, oxygen, and other things can pass between them.

▶ Birth

This is what normally happens:

9 months before birth
Fertilization.
Embryo starts to grow.

A few days before birth
The baby turns head down.

Just before birth
Contractions start - muscles round the womb squeeze up.
The cervix starts to open.
The baby's head passes into the vagina.
The bag bursts and the watery liquid runs out.

Birth
Contractions push the baby out.
The baby's lungs fill with air. From now on, the baby must take in its own oxygen and food.

Just after birth
Contractions push out the placenta (the 'afterbirth').
A doctor or nurse cuts the umbilical cord. The remains of the cord will shrivel away to leave the 'belly button'.

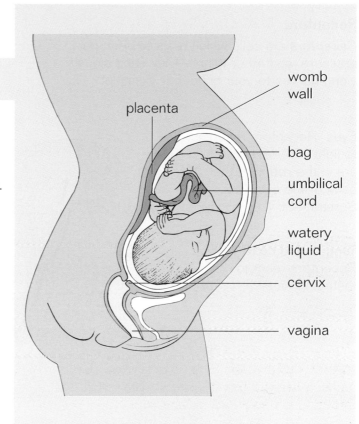

placenta
womb wall
bag
umbilical cord
watery liquid
cervix
vagina

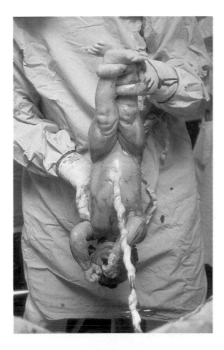

1 *umbilical cord*   *embryo*
   placenta   *bag of watery liquid*

Write down which of the above things does each of these:
   a Protects a baby in the womb from jolts and bumps.
   b Links the baby to the placenta.
   c Grows into the womb lining so that things can pass between the mother's blood and the baby's.

2 Copy these sentences in the correct order.
   The baby turns head down.
   The umbilical cord is cut.
   Contractions push the afterbirth out.
   The embryo grows into a baby.
   The embryo sinks into the womb lining.
   Contractions push the baby out. .

3 Explain how a baby gets its food and oxygen when it is in the womb.

Nerves and hormones

▶ Receptors

Receptors are cells which react to heat, pain, pressure, and other things. They send signals along nerves to your brain. For example:

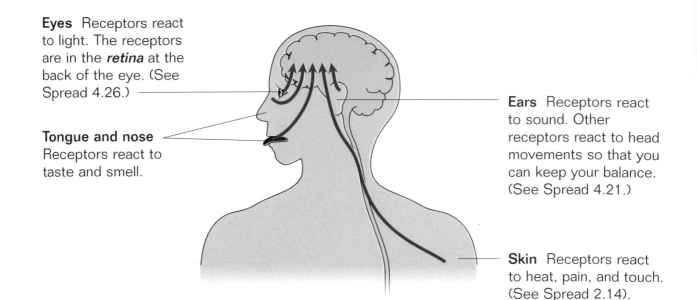

Eyes Receptors react to light. The receptors are in the *retina* at the back of the eye. (See Spread 4.26.)

Tongue and nose Receptors react to taste and smell.

Ears Receptors react to sound. Other receptors react to head movements so that you can keep your balance. (See Spread 4.21.)

Skin Receptors react to heat, pain, and touch. (See Spread 2.14).

▶ Working together

The different parts of your body must work together. To do this, they send messages to each other using *nerves* and *hormones*:

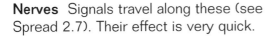

Nerves Signals travel along these (see Spread 2.7). Their effect is very quick.

Hormones These are chemicals which control how different organs work. They are made in the *endocrine glands* and carried in the blood. Their effect can be slow.

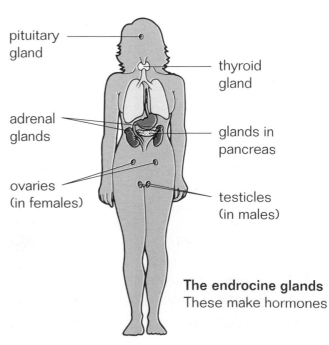

pituitary gland

thyroid gland

adrenal glands

glands in pancreas

ovaries (in females)

testicles (in males)

The endocrine glands
These make hormones

Here are some examples of hormones:

Hormone	Where made	Main effect
human growth hormone	pituitary gland	controls how the body grows
insulin	glands in pancreas	controls the amount of sugar in the blood
adrenalin	adrenal glands	speeds up the heart and breathing
oestrogen	ovaries	controls female sexual features
testosterone	testicles	controls male sexual features

▶ Using hormones

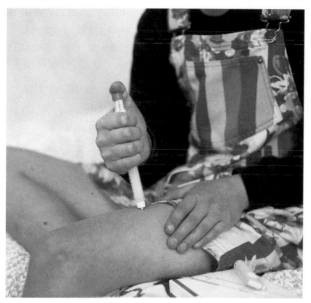

People with *diabetes* do not make enough insulin. So their blood sugar level can get dangerously high. They must be careful with their diet and may need insulin injections.

In a woman, the release of eggs is controlled by hormones. *Fertility drugs* act like hormones. They can lead to twins, triplets, or even more babies.

---

1 Choose the word on the right which goes with each of these:
   a These react to heat, pain, touch, and other things.
   b These carry signals from receptors to the brain.
   c These chemicals control how different organs work.

   > hormones
   > glands
   > nerves
   > receptors

2 In the table at the top of the page, find the names of these:
   a The hormone which speeds up the heart and breathing.
   b The glands that make this hormone.
   c The hormone which controls the amount of sugar in the blood.

3 Explain why diabetics need to inject themselves with insulin.

Skin

▶ Skin features

Your body is covered in skin:

Skin is flexible It can stretch and bend.

Skin keeps out germs Germs can't easily get through skin, unless you cut yourself.

Skin has receptors in These are special cells that react to touch, pain, and heat (see Spread 2.13).

Skin is waterproof It keeps out water.

Skin has melanin in This is a brown substance that protects you from the Sun's ultraviolet rays. Dark skin has more melanin than pale skin.

Skin gets worn away Dead cells on the outside are slowly replaced by the cells growing underneath.

Inside your skin:

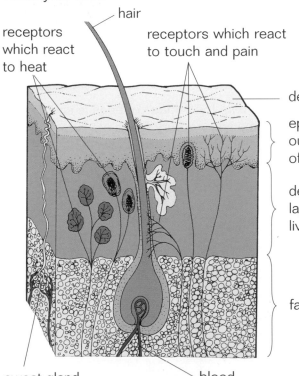

hair

receptors which react to heat

receptors which react to touch and pain

dead cells

epidermis: outer layer of cells

dermis: layer of living cells

fatty layer

sweat gland (makes sweat)

blood

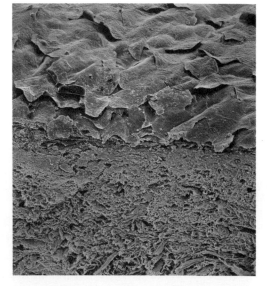

Human skin, magnified 150 times. The flat shapes at the top are dead cells.

► Keeping a steady temperature

To work properly, the inside of your body must stay at a steady temperature of about 37 °C. Your skin helps to keep you at the right temperature:

Cooling down

Your body is usually warmer than the air around it. So you lose heat through your skin.

If you get too hot, *sweat* comes out of your skin. When sweat evaporates, it quickly carries heat away. This cools you down.

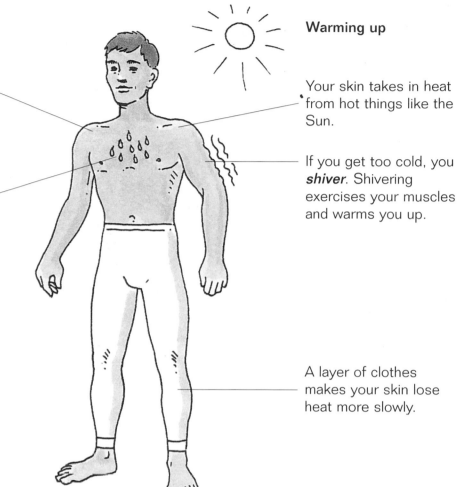

Warming up

Your skin takes in heat from hot things like the Sun.

If you get too cold, you *shiver*. Shivering exercises your muscles and warms you up.

A layer of clothes makes your skin lose heat more slowly.

1 The diagram on the right shows part of your skin. Copy the diagram and write in these labels:
   dead cells   hair   sweat gland   receptor

2 Write down two jobs done by the skin.

3 Copy and complete this sentence:
   The inside of your body must stay at a steady temperature of....

4 Describe one way in which your body can cool down if it gets too hot.

5 Describe one way in which your body can warm up if it gets too cold.

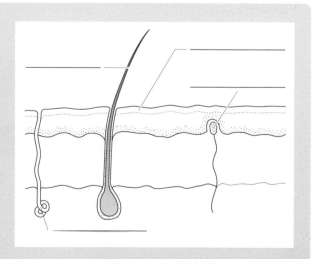

The food you need

Food is a mixture of useful substances - carbohydrates, fats, proteins, fibre, minerals, vitamins, and water. A *balanced* diet is one which gives you the right amounts of all of them.

Carbohydrates

These supply about half of your energy. The body may also change them into fats.

Examples

Sugar in...
jams, cakes, sweets, fruit

Starch in...
potatoes, rice, bread, flour

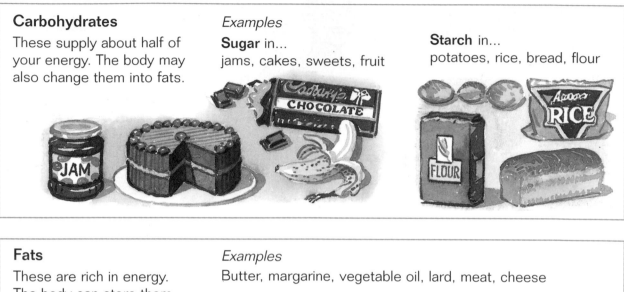

Fats

These are rich in energy. The body can store them to use later.

Examples

Butter, margarine, vegetable oil, lard, meat, cheese

Proteins

These are for body-building. You need them for growth and for replacing dead cells.

Examples

Meat, eggs, fish, milk, cheese, bread

Minerals

Your body needs small amounts of these.

Examples

Calcium (for making bones and teeth) from cheese, milk
Iron (for making blood) from liver, eggs, bread

Vitamins

Your body needs small amounts of these.

Examples

Vitamin A	Vitamin B_1	Vitamin B_2	Vitamin C	Vitamin D
Margarine, butter, liver, carrots, green vegetables, fish oil	Yeast, bread, meat, milk, potatoes	Milk, liver, eggs, cheese	Blackcurrants, green vegetables, oranges	Margarine, eggs, fish oil

Fibre

You can't digest fibre. But it is good for you because it helps food pass through your gut more easily.

Examples

Vegetables, cereals, bread

Water

You need about a litre of water every day - more if it is hot or you are very active.

Examples

Drinks, fruits and other foods with water in

1 *proteins   carbohydrates   fats   vitamins*
   Copy these sentences. Fill in the blanks, choosing words from those above.
      You need ____ and ____ for energy.
      You need ____ for growth.

2 Copy the chart on the right.
   The tick shows that bread has lots of carbohydrate in it. Put in more ticks to complete the chart.

3 Write down *two* foods with *calcium* in.

4 Write down *two* foods with *fibre* in.

5 Write down *two* foods with *vitamin C* in.

6 Copy and complete these sentences:
   a Your body needs calcium because......
   b Your body needs fibre because....

Food ▼	carbo-hydrate	fat	protein
bread	✓		
milk			
cheese			

Germs and diseases

▶ Microbes

Microbes are tiny living things that can only be seen with a microscope. There are billions in the air, soil, water, and our bodies. The harmful ones are called *germs*. They cause disease.

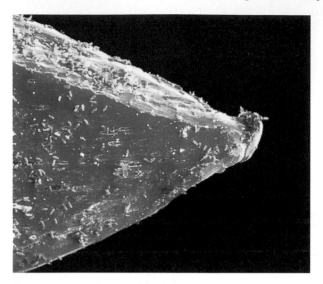

Bacteria on the tip of a hypodermic needle, magnified 400 times.

Bacteria and viruses are microbes:

Bacteria are living cells. They can *multiply* very quickly - until there are millions of them.

Diseases caused by bacteria - examples
Sore throats, pneumonia, food poisoning.

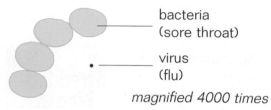

bacteria
(sore throat)

virus
(flu)

magnified 4000 times

Viruses are smaller than bacteria. They invade your cells and stop them working properly.

Diseases caused by viruses - examples
Flu, chicken-pox, colds

▶ Fighting disease

If germs get into your body, your white blood cells attack them. Some cells make chemicals called *antibodies* which kill germs.

If you have had chicken-pox, you probably won't catch it again. You are *immune* to it. That is because you already have antibodies for the disease, so you are ready for the next attack.

Medicines help fight disease:

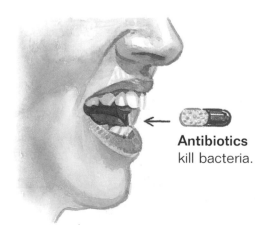

Antibiotics
kill bacteria.

Vaccines have weak or dead germs put in them. Your white blood cells make antibodies for these germs. So, when the real disease strikes, your body is ready to fight it.

▶ Spreading germs

An invasion of germs is called an *infection*.
Germs can spread like this:

Droplets in the air When you cough or sneeze, you spray droplets into the air. These carry germs which other people breathe in.

Example
Catching flu or a cold.

Animals Insects may leave germs on food. Or they may leave germs in the blood when they bite.

Example
Blood-sucking mosquitoes spreading malaria.

Contact You can pick up some germs by touching an infected person or thing.

Example
Catching chicken-pox.

Dirty food and water Germs from toilet waste can get into food and water.

Example
Handling food after using the toilet.

1 *germs   infection   vaccine   immune   antibodies   antibiotics*
  Copy these sentences. Fill in the blanks, choosing words from those above.
  a Harmful microbes are called ____.
  b An invasion of germs is called an ____.
  c If you are ____ to a disease, you won't catch it again.
  d Some white blood cells make ____ which kill germs.
  e A ____ has weak or dead germs in it.

2 Look at the diagram on the right. Write down *three* ways in which germs might get into the boy's body.

3 Explain why you should wash your hands after using the toilet.

Healthy living

To help your health, you need to do these things:

Eat sensibly

Take plenty of exercise

Avoid health risks

▶ Diet

- If you do not eat enough fruit and vegetables, you may not get enough vitamins and fibre.

- Too little fibre makes you constipated and may cause disease in the gut.

- Too much fat makes you overweight and may cause heart disease.

▶ Health risks

Smoking This causes heart attacks, blocked arteries, lung cancer, and difficult breathing.

Solvents These are in glue and paint. Sniffing them is very dangerous. It damages the lungs and brain.

Alcohol This slows your reactions. Heavy drinking damages the liver, heart, and stomach.

Drugs Some of these are *addictive*. When the body gets used to them, it cannot do without them.

AIDS

AIDS is a disease that can't yet be cured. It is caused by a virus called **HIV**.

People with the virus are **HIV positive**. But it may be many years before they develop AIDS.

HIV attacks white blood cells, so the body can't defend itself against disease.

HIV can only be passed to others in three ways:

- When two people are having sex.
- By blood-to-blood contact.
- From an infected mother to her unborn baby.

If a man wears a condom while having sex, there is less chance of HIV being passed on.

▶ Health before birth

A mother must look after her baby *before* it is born.

Smoking If she smokes, her baby may be born underweight.

Alcohol If she drinks alcohol, her baby may be harmed. Also, it may be born too early.

German measles (rubella)
If she catches German measles in the first three months of pregnancy, her baby may be born deaf, blind, or with heart trouble.

That is why girls are given injections to stop them catching German measles.

---

1 The sentences below have got the wrong endings.
   Write them out so that the correct parts go together.

Smoking is bad for you because...	...it helps prevent constipation.
A pregnant woman shouldn't smoke because...	...it contains vitamins and fibre.
Too much alcohol is bad for you because...	...they damage your lungs and brain.
Solvents are bad for you because...	...it causes lung cancer and heart disease.
Fibre is good for you because...	...her baby may be born underweight.
Fruit is good for you because...	...it damages your liver.

2 Explain why girls are given injections to stop them catching German measles.

Sorting and grouping

Look at these two animals.

They have some features which are *similar:*

They have some features which are *different:*

- One beak
- Two eyes
- Lots of feathers

- Length of beak
- Position of eyes
- Colour of feathers

Scientists use *similar* features to put things into groups.

The two animals are both in a group called **birds**.

Scientists use *different* features to tell things apart.

One bird is an **owl**. The other bird is a **gull**.

▶ Keys

Here are four insects:

A   B   C   D

The table on the right is called a **key**.
Use it to work out the name of insect **A**.

Start at number 1.
See which description is the best match.
Go to another number if you are told to.
See which name you end up at.

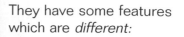

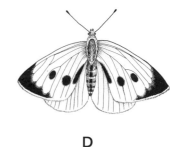

Key

1	Wings	Go to **2**
	No wings to be seen	Earwig
2	One pair of wings	Housefly
	Two pairs of wings	Go to **3**
3	Wing larger than body	Butterfly
	Wing smaller than body	Wasp

Here are four plants:

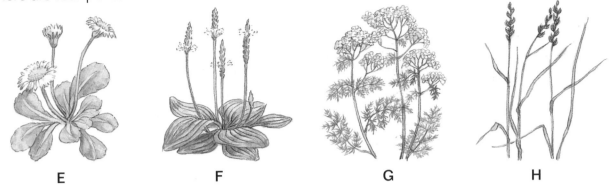

E   F   G   H

The chart below is another type of key. Use it to work out the name of plant **E**.

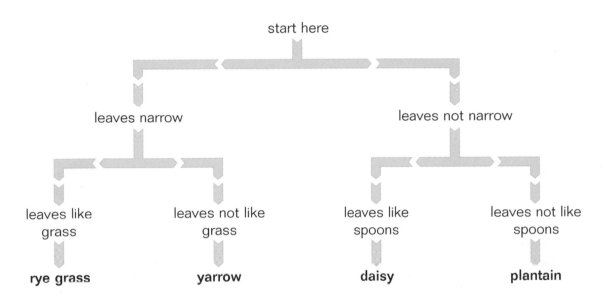

start here

leaves narrow   leaves not narrow

leaves like grass   leaves not like grass   leaves like spoons   leaves not like spoons

rye grass   **yarrow**   **daisy**   **plantain**

Start at the top.
See which description is the best match.
Follow that line to the next description.... and so on.
See which name you end up at.

1 Look at the two animals on the right.
  a Write down *three* features they have which are *similar*
  b Write down *three* features they have which are *different*.

2 Use the key on the left-hand page to work out the names of insects **B**, **C**, and **D**.

3 Use the key on this page to work out the names of plants **F**, **G**, and **H**.

2.19 More sorting and grouping

Scientists think that all living things are related. They sort them into groups with similar features. The biggest groups of all are called **kingdoms**. You can see them on the next page.

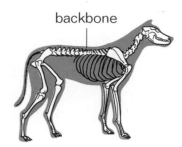

backbone

▶ Animals with backbones

In the animal kingdom, animals with backbones are called **vertebrates**. There are five main groups:

Fish

Fins
Covered in scales
Live in water
Gills for breathing
Lay eggs
Body temperature changes

Examples Shark, herring, cod

Reptiles

Covered in dry scales
Most live on land
Lungs for breathing
Lay eggs
Body temperature changes

Examples Crocodile, tortoise, lizard

Amphibians

Covered in moist skin
Live in water and on land
Adults have lungs for breathing
Lay eggs, usually in water
Body temperature changes

Examples Newt, toad, frog

Birds

Covered in feathers
Lungs for breathing
Lay eggs
Steady body temperature

Examples Robin, penguin, blackbird

Mammals

Covered in hairy skin
Lungs for breathing
Most give birth to babies and do not lay eggs
Mother makes milk for babies
Steady body temperature

Examples Cat, human, whale, mouse

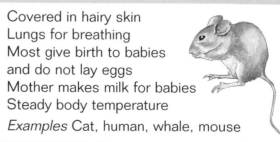

Feature ▼	Fish	Amphibians	Reptiles	Birds	Mammals
backbone					
lungs					
scales					
feathers					
hair					
lay eggs					
born as babies					✓
steady body temperature					

1 Copy the table on the left. The tick shows that most mammals have babies.

   Put in more ticks to complete the table.

   Put a big 'H' at the bottom of the column that humans are in.

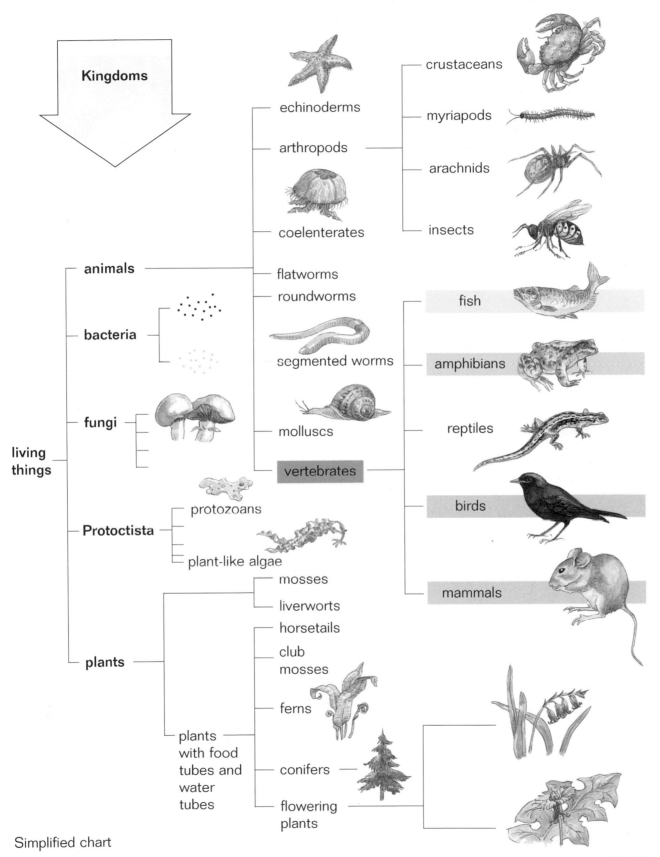

Kingdoms

living things
- **animals**
  - echinoderms
  - arthropods
    - crustaceans
    - myriapods
    - arachnids
    - insects
  - coelenterates
  - flatworms
  - roundworms
  - segmented worms
  - molluscs
  - vertebrates
    - fish
    - amphibians
    - reptiles
    - birds
    - mammals
- **bacteria**
- **fungi**
- **Protoctista**
  - protozoans
  - plant-like algae
- **plants**
  - mosses
  - liverworts
  - plants with food tubes and water tubes
    - horsetails
    - club mosses
    - ferns
    - conifers
    - flowering plants

Simplified chart

51

2.20 Variation

▶ **Varying features**

People are never exactly alike. Look at the family on the opposite page. Their features are not all the same. There is **variation** from one person to another.

Here are some features which can vary:

height
colour of hair
colour of eyes
shape of nose
weight
blood group

Your different features are sometimes called your **characteristics**.

Like all living things, these dogs show variation.

▶ **Features passed on...**

Some features are **inherited**. You are born with them. There were passed on to you by your parents.

Tim and Jim are 'identical twins'. They inherited the same features from their parents. For example, they inherited their mother's black hair.

...and not passed on

Some features are not inherited. You are not born with them. You get them as you go through life

Tim and Jim are not *exactly* alike. Jim has bigger muscles because he trains in the gym. He did not inherit his big muscles. They will not be passed on to his children.

Mixing up features

The children below have inherited some features from their
mother and some from their father. But it was a matter of chance
which features came from which parent:

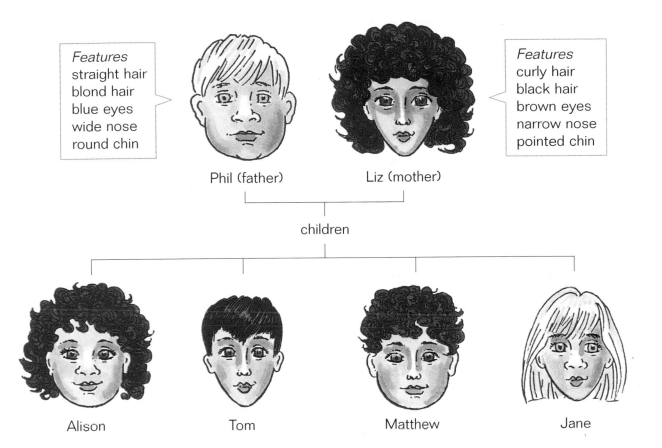

Features
straight hair
blond hair
blue eyes
wide nose
round chin

Phil (father)

Liz (mother)

Features
curly hair
black hair
brown eyes
narrow nose
pointed chin

children

Alison

Tom

Matthew

Jane

1 Look at the dogs in the photograph on the opposite page.
Write down *two* features which show variation.

2 In the family above, Alison
has inherited her mother's
curly, black hair and brown
eyes, and her father's wide
nose and round chin.

Copy the table on the right.
Complete it to show the
features which the other
children have inherited from
each parent.

3 A person can have features
which are not inherited.
Write down one example.

	Alison	Tom	Matthew	Jane
hair type*	mother's			
hair colour	mother's			
eye colour	mother's			
nose shape	father's			
chin shape	father's			

* hair type = straight or curly

2.21 Genes in action

▶ Chromosomes and genes

Information about all your features is stored in your cells. It is stored in **chromosomes**, as a complicated chemical code.

Chromosome Most human cells have 46 chromosomes. These store all the chemical instructions needed to build a complete human body and make it work.

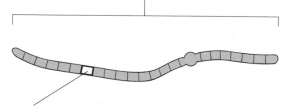

Human cell

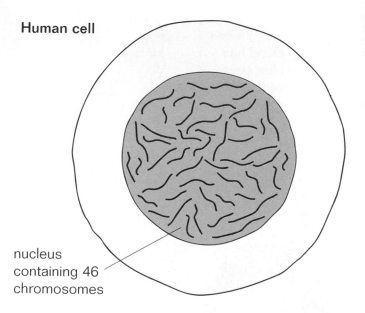

nucleus containing 46 chromosomes

Gene This is one short bit of a chromosome. It stores the instructions for one feature - for example, hair colour. In all 46 chromosomes, you have about 60 000 genes!

▶ Passing on genes

A baby develops from a fertilized egg (see Spreads 2.11 and 2.12). It gets half its genes from each parent:

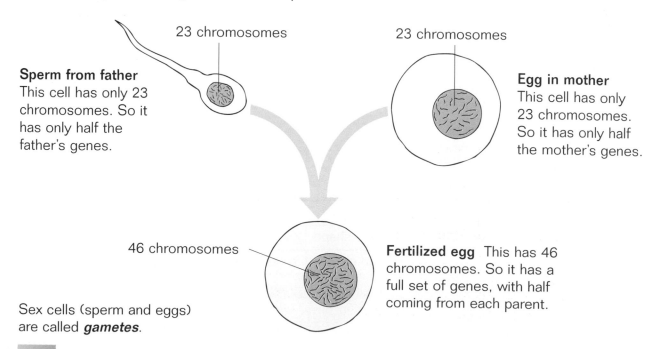

23 chromosomes

23 chromosomes

Sperm from father
This cell has only 23 chromosomes. So it has only half the father's genes.

Egg in mother
This cell has only 23 chromosomes. So it has only half the mother's genes.

46 chromosomes

Fertilized egg This has 46 chromosomes. So it has a full set of genes, with half coming from each parent.

Sex cells (sperm and eggs) are called **gametes**.

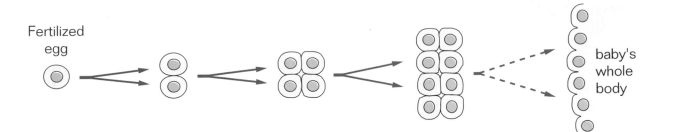

Fertilized egg

baby's whole body

A fertilized egg grows and split to form two cells. Each cell has a full set of genes.

The cells split again.... and again.... and so on. It takes over a million cells to make a baby.

▶ The same genes

These identical twins have exactly the same genes because then came from the same fertilized egg. When the egg split to make two cells, each developed into a separate baby.

To get more plants, gardeners can take cuttings. A cutting grows roots and becomes a new plant. The new plant is just like the old one because it has the same genes.

1 Choose the word on the right which goes with each of the following:
  a These each have a nucleus.
  b These each store information about one feature.
  c In most of your cells, there are 46 of these.
  d These have only half the genes of most cells.

| chromosomes |
| cells |
| sperms |
| genes |

2 Copy these sentences. Writing *TRUE* or *FALSE* after each one.
  Identical twins have exactly the same genes.
  A mother and daughter have exactly the same genes.
  A plant and its cuttings have exactly the same genes.

Living places

▶ **Habitats**

The place where an animal or plant lives is called its *habitat*. It is usually shared with other animals and plants.

A frog's habitat is in and around a pond, where it is wet and shady. A frog needs these conditions to stop its skin drying out.

Here are some of the *factors* which affect living things and their habitats:

Non-living factors

Climate Some places are hotter, wetter, or windier than others.

Days and seasons It is warmer and lighter in the day than at night. It is warmer in summer than in winter.

Landscape It is more sheltered in a valley than on a hill or the coast.

Soil Clay soils hold water. Sandy soils dry quickly. Some soils have lime in them. Others have acid. This affects how plants grow.

Living factors

Other living things

Plants stop other plants getting light and water.

Animals eat plants and other animals.

Humans take over land for crops. They dig soil and cut down trees.

Pollution

Pollution can harm living things and their habitats.
Humans are to blame for pollution.

Harmful gases These come from power stations, factories, cars, and trucks.

Factory waste Poisonous chemicals may be dumped into rivers or the sea.

Sewage This is often dumped at sea. The germs in it are harmful to health.

Fertilizers and pesticides These chemicals are put on crops to help them grow. But if the chemicals run into lakes and rivers, they harm the wildlife there.

Oil This sometimes spills from tankers. It kills sea-birds and fish, and ruins beaches.

---

1 Here are four animals:

human   polar bear   frog   camel

Write down the animal which does each of these:
a Lives in a wet, shady habitat.
b Lives in a cold, icy habitat.
c Causes pollution.

2 Write down *three* ways in which a river might become polluted.

3 Copy and complete these sentences with your own words:
a A plant can stop another plant growing because...
b An animal can stop a plant growing because...

Features for living

Animals and plants have special features to help them survive
in their habitat. They are **adapted** to their way of life.

▶ Surviving the winter

This robin fluffs up its feathers when cold. The feathers
trap air like a sleeping bag or duvet.

Many trees lose their leaves in the
autumn. Without leaves, they need
less water. So they can survive
when the ground is frozen.

▶ Camouflage

Peppered moths are difficult to see against a
tree. So they probably won't get eaten by a bird.

There is a leaf insect in this photograph.
Can you find it? (See also Question 2)

▶ Catching food

The chameleon has a long tongue which it flicks out to catch insects.

The chameleon is also very good at camouflage. It can change colour to match its background.

This owl has special features to help it catch and eat its food (see Question 1).

1 Look at the owl in the photograph (above right). Write down the features you think the owl has to help it:
   a hunt at night.
   b grip small animals.
   c tear small animals apart.
   d keep warm.

2 Look at the photograph on the left.
The leaf insect looks like a leaf. Explain why this helps it survive.

3 Look at the diagram on the right and the sentences below. They are about some of our human features.

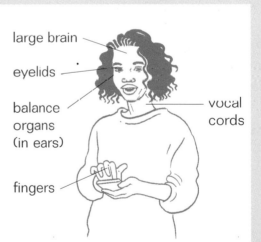

The sentences have the wrong endings. Write them out so that the correct parts go together.

We have eyelids...	...to stop us falling over.
We have fingers...	...so that we can speak.
We have a large brain...	...for holding and moving things carefully.
We have balance organs...	...to clear dust from our eyes when we blink.
We have vocal cords...	...so that we can think and remember, and understand our language.

Chains and webs

▶ Food chains

All living things need food. It gives them energy and the substances they need to build their bodies.

A **food chain** shows how living things feed on other living things. In the food chain below, the blackbird feeds on the snail, and the snail feeds on the leaf:

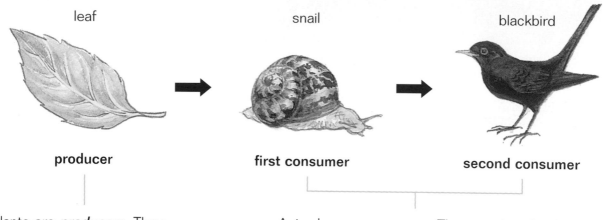

leaf   snail   blackbird

producer   **first consumer**   **second consumer**

Plants are **producers**. They produce (make) their own food.

Animals are **consumers**. They get their food by consuming (eating) other living things.

▶ Predators and prey

Animals which kill and eat other animals are called **predators**. The animals they kill and eat are their **prey**.

Here are some examples:

Predator	Prey
blackbird	worms insects snails
lion	zebra antelope wildebeest
wolf	reindeer moose
fox	rabbits mice birds

predator

prey

▶ Food webs

Many animals eat more than one type of food. So living things can be part of several food chains. The result is a **food web**. Here is an example:

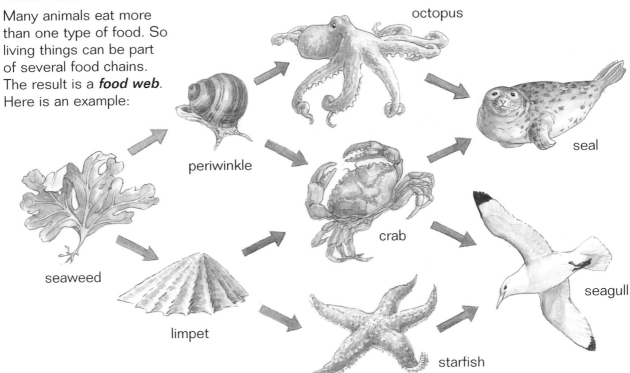

octopus

seal

periwinkle

crab

seaweed

limpet

starfish

seagull

▶ Pollution problems

If poisonous chemicals get into a food chain or web, they can kill lots of living things.

Look at the food web above. If poisonous chemicals are dumped at sea, they may be sucked in by *limpets*. So they will end up in the bodies of all these animals:

crabs   starfish   seals   seagulls

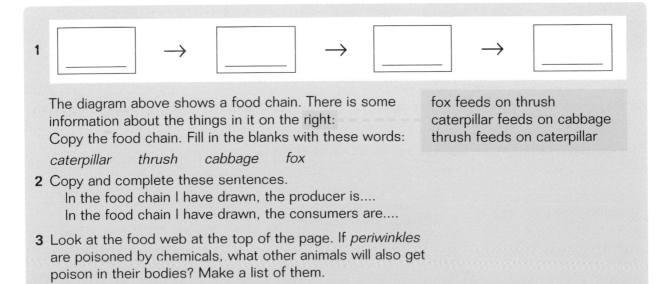

1

The diagram above shows a food chain. There is some information about the things in it on the right:
Copy the food chain. Fill in the blanks with these words:

caterpillar   thrush   cabbage   fox

fox feeds on thrush
caterpillar feeds on cabbage
thrush feeds on caterpillar

2 Copy and complete these sentences.
   In the food chain I have drawn, the producer is....
   In the food chain I have drawn, the consumers are....

3 Look at the food web at the top of the page. If *periwinkles* are poisoned by chemicals, what other animals will also get poison in their bodies? Make a list of them.

2.25 Microbes and rotting

Microbes are tiny living things that can only be seen with a microscope (see also Spread 2.16).

▶ **Decomposers**

Some microbes feed on the remains of dead plants and animals. They make the dead things rot by turning them into a liquid. This is their food.

Microbes which make things rot are called *decomposers*.

Rotting is also called *decay*.

Decomposer microbes are useful:

As the apple rots, it turns into a liquid.

The liquid soaks into the soil.

The liquid puts useful substances back into the soil. New plants need these for growth.

▶ **More and more microbes**

If the conditions are right, microbes can grow and *multiply*:

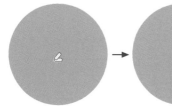 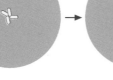  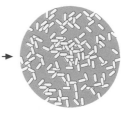

As they grow, they split..   ..and split..   ..and split..   ..until there are millions.

To grow and multiply, most decomposer microbes need these:

Warmth The microbes work best when it is warm (about 35 °C).

Damp The microbes need water.

Air Most microbes need oxygen. (However, some can live without oxygen.)

▶ Microbes at work

In a compost heap, microbes turn plant clippings into rich compost for the soil.

In a sewage works, microbes turn waste from humans into gas and fertilizer.

▶ Rot or not

Some materials rot....

....others do not.

Biodegradable materials

These are materials which rot.
They come from plants and animals.

Examples

meat	vegetables	fruit	
cotton	paper	wood	wool

Non-biodegradable materials

These are materials which do not rot.

Examples

metals	glass	china
stone	plastic	

1 a Explain what *biodegradable* means.
   b Copy the table on the right. Put a ✓ or a ✗ against each material to show whether it is biodegradable or not.

2 Copy and complete these sentences:
   Microbes which make things rot are called......
   Rotting is also called......
   When something rots, it is turned into a......
   Rotting plants are good for the soil because......

3 To grow and multiply, most decomposer microbes need *three* things, as well as food. Write down these three things.

	Biodegradable
fruit	
stone	
paper	
glass	
cotton	
wood	

Nature's recycling

▶ Elements in living things

Like everything else, living things are made from simple substances called **elements** (see Spread 3.4). These join together to make the different materials in their bodies.

Elements in your body

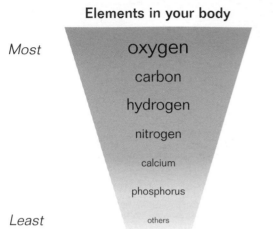

Most

oxygen

carbon

hydrogen

nitrogen

calcium

phosphorus

Least   others

4% carbon

20% carbon

90% carbon

Humans, grass, and coal all have **carbon** in them. (Coal was formed from plants which died millions of years ago.)

▶ Recycling in action

As living things grow and die, the elements in them are **recycled** - they are used over and over again. On the right, you can see how this can happen.

animals eat plants

dead plants
dead animals
animal droppings

growing plants

The carbon in living things is recycled. This is called the **carbon cycle**. You can see it on the opposite page.

decomposer microbes at work

liquid in soil

64

The carbon cycle

Plants take carbon dioxide from the atmosphere. They use it to make their food by photosynthesis (see Spread 2.2).

When animals breathe, they put carbon dioxide into the atmosphere. Some decomposer microbes also put carbon dioxide into the atmosphere.

When fuels and fires burn, they put carbon dioxide into the atmosphere.

← flow of carbon

carbon dioxide in atmosphere

burning

respiration

photosynthesis

feeding

plants

animals

ancient plants and sea creatures

decomposer microbes

decomposer microbes

fossil fuels

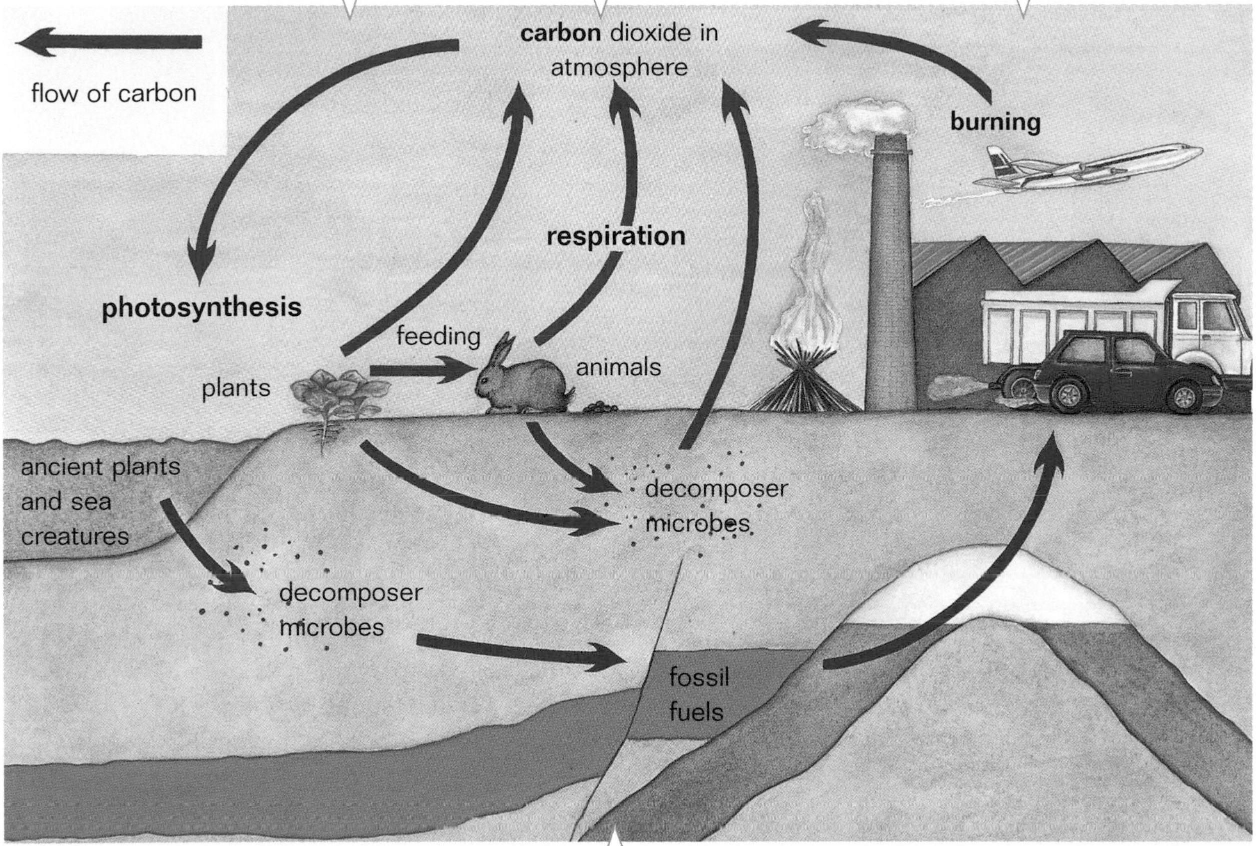

Coal, oil, and natural gas are called **fossil fuels**. They formed from the remains of plants and tiny sea creatures which died millions of years ago.

1 Write down the *four* main elements in the human body.

2 Look at the diagram of the carbon cycle above.
   a Write down *one* thing that takes carbon dioxide out of the atmosphere.
   b Write down *two* things that put carbon dioxide into the atmosphere.
   c Write down *three* fuels with carbon in.

3 Look at the diagram on the left. Then copy and complete these sentences:
   Elements in plants can end up in animals because....
   Elements in old plants can end up in new plants because....

Problems in the air

▶ Global warming

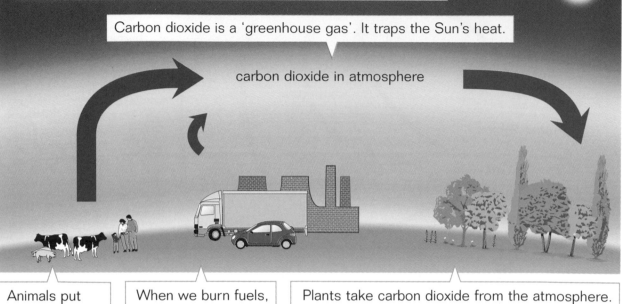

Some gases in the atmosphere act like the glass in a greenhouse. They trap the Sun's heat. This is called the *greenhouse effect*.

Carbon dioxide is a 'greenhouse gas'. It traps the Sun's heat.

carbon dioxide in atmosphere

Animals put carbon dioxide into the atmosphere.

When we burn fuels, we put extra carbon dioxide into the atmosphere.

Plants take carbon dioxide from the atmosphere. But they cannot take in all the extra. So more of the Sun's heat is trapped and the Earth warms up. This is called *global warming*.

Methane is another greenhouse gas. It comes from oil and gas rigs like the one above. But it mainly comes from swamps, cattle waste, and rice fields.

Destroying forests adds to global warming. When forests burn, they put extra carbon dioxide into the atmosphere. Also, there are fewer trees left to take in carbon dioxide.

▶ The ozone layer

High in the atmosphere, there is thin layer of a gas called **ozone**.

Ozone protects us from the Sun's harmful ultraviolet rays, which cause skin cancer.

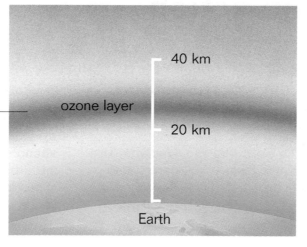

40 km

ozone layer

20 km

Earth

Ozone is destroyed by gases once used in fridges, freezers, aerosols, and in making foam packaging. So manufacturers now use 'ozone friendly' gases instead.

▶ Acid rain

Normal rain is slightly acid. But some of the exhaust gases from power stations and vehicles make it more acid. Acid rain harms plants and water life, and eats into stonework.

These gases cause acid rain:

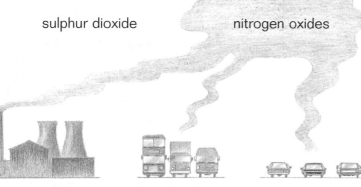

sulphur dioxide

nitrogen oxides

power stations (coal-burning)

diesel vehicles

cars without catalytic converters

One effect of acid rain.

---

1 Copy and complete these sentences:
   The *greenhouse effect* means that gases in the atmosphere are trapping.....
   The ozone layer protects us from....
   Acid rain is caused by gases from....

2 Write down the name of *one* gas that causes acid rain.

3 Write down the names of *two* 'greenhouse gases'.

4 Look at the list on the right. From this list, copy out the things which you think may add to global warming.

Using more vehicles

Using more electricity

Planting more trees

Breeding more cattle

Burning down forests

2.28 Cells in action

▶ Living cells

In cells (see Spread 2.1), all the processes of life take place. Here is some more information about them:

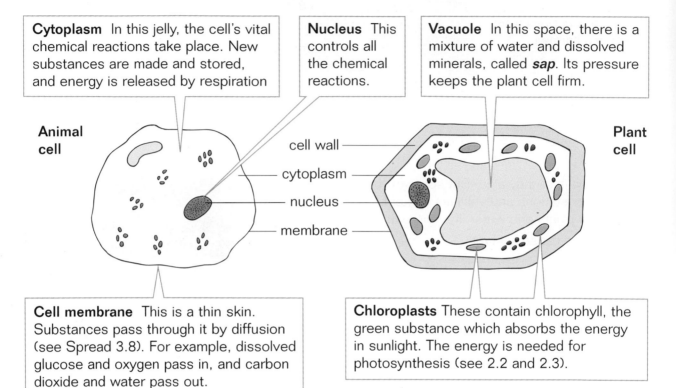

Cytoplasm In this jelly, the cell's vital chemical reactions take place. New substances are made and stored, and energy is released by respiration

Nucleus This controls all the chemical reactions.

Vacuole In this space, there is a mixture of water and dissolved minerals, called *sap*. Its pressure keeps the plant cell firm.

Animal cell

Plant cell

cell wall
cytoplasm
nucleus
membrane

Cell membrane This is a thin skin. Substances pass through it by diffusion (see Spread 3.8). For example, dissolved glucose and oxygen pass in, and carbon dioxide and water pass out.

Chloroplasts These contain chlorophyll, the green substance which absorbs the energy in sunlight. The energy is needed for photosynthesis (see 2.2 and 2.3).

▶ Groups of cells

In an animal or plant, different groups of cells have different jobs to do. Groups of similar cells are called *tissue*. A collection of tissues doing a particular job is an *organ*. The complete animal or plant is an *organism*.

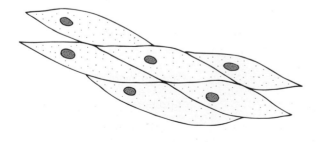

To make a muscle contract, these muscle cells shorten.

▶ Respiration

Cells need energy to live, move, and grow. They can get it by 'burning up' glucose. This is the process called *respiration*.

Here is a word equation for one form of respiration:

glucose + oxygen → carbon dioxide + water + *energy*

This type of respiration is called *aerobic respiration* ('aerobic' means 'using oxygen').

For a short time, cells can also get energy from glucose without using oxygen. This is called *anaerobic respiration*.

Animals get glucose by digesting their food. Plants make glucose by photosynthesis.

▶ Plant cells in action

Photosynthesis mainly takes place in leaf cells. Here is a word equation for what happens:

$$\text{carbon dioxide} + \text{water} + \textit{light energy} \rightarrow \text{glucose} + \text{oxygen}$$

Photosynthesis slows down if there is less carbon dioxide, or less water, or less light, or the temperature drops.

Palisade cells These make most of the glucose. They are near the top of the leaf where the light can reach them.

Stomata These are tiny holes that let gases (carbon dioxide, oxygen, and water vapour) in or out of the leaf. A single hole is a **stoma**.

Guard cells These shrink or swell to control the flow of gas through the stomata.

Xylem tubes These carry water and dissolved minerals from roots to leaves .

Phloem tubes These carry dissolved glucose to growing points or storage areas.

Root hair cells These take in water and minerals from the soil.

The upward flow of water through a plant is called the **transpiration stream**. Many leaves have a waxy layer on top to stop them losing too much water by evaporation.

Cells in a leaf

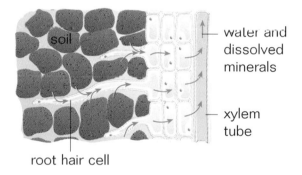

Cells in a root

1

oxygen	vacuole	carbon dioxide
stoma	water	chlorophyll
glucose	xylem tube	phloem tube

Choose the word or words above which go with each of the following:
a Small hole which lets gases in and out of a leaf.
b Green substance which absorbs the energy in sunlight.
c In a plant cell, this contains sap.
d This carries water and dissolved minerals up through a plant.
e Two substances produced during aerobic respiration.
f Two substances produced during photosynthesis.

2 Write down *two* things which a plant cell and an animal cell both have.
3 Write down *two* things which a plant cell has but an animal cell does *not* have.
4 Write down *three* things which are needed for photosynthesis.

EXTENSION

2.29 More about genes

Most of the cells in your body carry a full set of genes. The genes are in the chromosomes in the nucleus of each cell (See Spread 2.21).

▶ Pairs of genes and chromosomes

People inherit their chromosomes in pairs, with one coming from each parent. So they inherit their genes in pairs. For example:

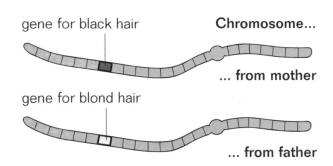

gene for black hair

Chromosome...

... from mother

gene for blond hair

... from father

If someone inherits a gene for blond hair from their father and a gene for black hair from their mother, their hair is black. A black hair gene is *dominant* over a blond hair gene.

Human cell

nucleus

1	2	3	4	5	6
7	8	9	10	11	12
13	14	15	16	17	18
19	20	21	22	23	

In humans, ordinary cells have 23 pairs of chromosomes, giving 46 in total.

When sex cells (sperms and eggs) are made, they only get *one* chromosome from each pair. So they only have *one* gene from each pair. However, *which* one is a matter of chance.

▶ Male and female

In a cell, one pair of chromosomes controls whether a baby develops as a boy or girl. These are the **sex chromosomes**. There are two types, called **X** and **Y**.

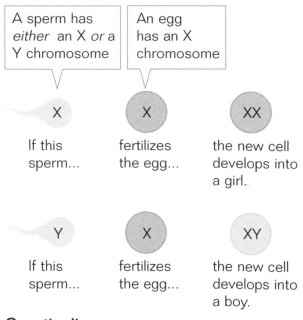

X
Y
male

X
X
female

In each ordinary cell, males have one X chromosome and a shorter Y chromosome. Females have two X chromosomes.

In sex cells, there is only one chromosome from each pair:

A sperm has *either* an X *or* a Y chromosome

An egg has an X chromosome

X

X

XX

If this sperm...

fertilizes the egg...

the new cell develops into a girl.

Y

X

XY

If this sperm...

fertilizes the egg...

the new cell develops into a boy.

▶ Genetic diseases

Some diseases are inherited. They are caused by faulty genes. **Genetic diseases** include sickle-cell anaemia and cystic fibrosis.

In some cases, parents can be **carriers** - they can pass on the faulty gene without having the disease themselves. For example, a person can only have cystic fibrosis if they inherit the faulty gene from *both* parents.

▶ Sexual and asexual reproduction

For humans to reproduce, a sperm must combine with an egg. This is an example of *sexual reproduction*. Two sex cells must combine - one from each parent.

Flowering plants reproduce sexually (see Spread 2.4). However, some can also reproduce in another way. They develop bulbs or runners which separate and grow as new plants. This is called *asexual reproduction*. The new plant has exactly the same genes as the one it came from.

▶ Selective breeding

People try to breed animals with special features: for example, sheep with plenty of wool, or horses that can run fast. To do this, they select the animals which will mate (have sex). This is called *selective breeding*. The idea is that the 'babies' may inherit the best features of both parents. But chance still affects the result. If two champion racehorses mate, their foal may not be a champion.

Selective breeding is also used with plants to get better crops.

1 How many chromosomes are there in a human cell (not a sex cell)?

2 How many chromosomes are there in a human sperm?

3 How many chromosomes are there in a human egg?

4 Say whether each of these is an example of *sexual* or *asexual* reproduction:
   a A cat giving birth to a kitten.
   b A new plant growing from a cutting.
   c A seed developing after a flower has been pollinated.

5 How does someone get a *genetic* disease?

6 Copy and complete this chart to show what can happen when a sperm and egg join to make the first cell of a new baby:

Sex chromosomes in...			Baby
sperm	egg	baby	girl or boy
		XX	
		XY	

You need to put Xs and Ys in the first two columns, and 'boy' or 'girl' in each blank space in the last column.

2.30 Evolution

▶ Species

There are over a million different types of organism (living thing) on Earth. Each type is called a *species*.

Members of one species breed among themselves, but members of different species do not.

▶ The theory of evolution

In time, over many generations, a species can change. This is called *evolution*. If members of a species live and breed in separate groups, each group may evolve in a different way and new species may develop.

Scientists think that *all* species evolved from the same, simple organisms that developed on Earth about 3500 million years ago. They call this the *theory of evolution*.

Scientists learn about evolution by studying fossils (see Spread 3.21). The chart shows some of the stages in the evolution of mammals.

▶ The theory of natural selection

In 1858, Charles Darwin put forward an idea to explain how evolution might take place. He called it the *theory of natural selection*.

On the next page, there is an example of how natural selection works. The three pictures show how long necks might evolve in one species.

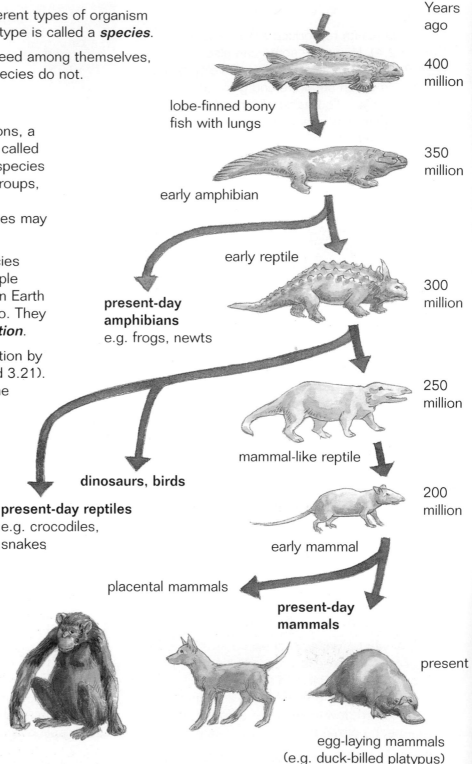

Years ago

400 million
lobe-finned bony fish with lungs

350 million
early amphibian

early reptile

present-day amphibians
e.g. frogs, newts

300 million

250 million
mammal-like reptile

dinosaurs, birds

present-day reptiles
e.g. crocodiles, snakes

200 million
early mammal

placental mammals

present-day mammals

present

egg-laying mammals
(e.g. duck-billed platypus)

Variation Each animal is a bit different from the others. By chance, one animal has inherited a long neck. This is useful for reaching food.

Selection Long-neck gets food while others starve. In this way, long-neck is 'selected' for survival and lives long enough to mate.

Adaptation Later generations inherit the long neck. The species becomes *adapted* to its living conditions (see 2.23)

▶ **Mutations**

The genes in 'baby' organisms are copies of genes in the parents. But sometimes, errors are made during copying. The genetic changes are called *mutations*. They happen at random and can produce completely new features - such as extra toes or a different skin colour. They are the main cause of variation.

▶ **Extinction**

In time, a species may die out: it may become *extinct*.

Extinction happens when a species does not adapt to changing conditions - new predators, new rivals for food, new diseases, or a change in climate.

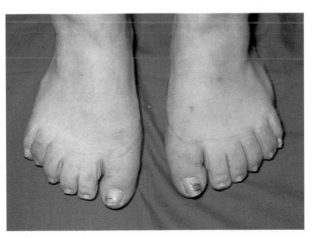

The result of a mutation.

1 From the chart on the opposite page, give *three* groups of animals living today that have evolved from early reptiles.

2 Look at the three pictures at the top of this page.
   a In the *second* picture, why does one animal live longer than the others?
   b In the *third* picture, why have all the animals got long necks?

3 *mutation adaptation species extinction*

   Which word means each of these?
   a Dying out.
   b Random genetic change.
   c Change to suit living conditions.

2.31 Food and energy

▶ Digesting food

During digestion, food is broken down into substances which will dissolve. This job is done by **enzymes** (see Spreads 2.8 and 3.26). For example, **amylase** in saliva (spit) is the enzyme which breaks down starch into sugar.

▶ Absorbing food

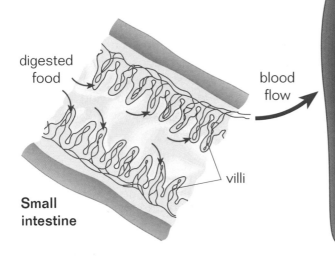

digested food

blood flow

villi

Small intestine

The inner surface of the small intestine is covered with million of tiny bumps called **villi**, with lots of blood capillaries in them. Together, they have a huge surface area for absorbing digested food into the blood.

▶ Energy in food

The chart on the right shows how much energy your body gets from different foods. The energy is measured in **kilojoules (kJ)**. One kilojoule is 1000 joules (see 4.13).

About half the energy in your food is used to drive vital body processes - like circulating the blood and keeping you warm. The rest is used to move your muscles.

If you eat more food than your body needs for energy and growth, the extra is stored as fat.

▶ The liver at work

Blood carries digested food to the liver for more processing. Here are some of the jobs done by the liver as blood passes through it:

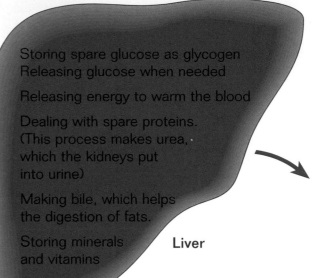

Storing spare glucose as glycogen
Releasing glucose when needed

Releasing energy to warm the blood

Dealing with spare proteins. (This process makes urea, which the kidneys put into urine)

Making bile, which helps the digestion of fats.

Storing minerals and vitamins

Liver

Homeostasis Temperature, glucose level, and amount of water are just some of the factors which must be kept steady in the body. Keeping conditions steady is called **homeostasis**. The liver is one of the organs that helps do the job.

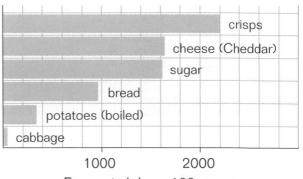

crisps
cheese (Cheddar)
sugar
bread
potatoes (boiled)
cabbage

1000   2000

Energy in kJ per 100 grams

▶ Food chains and pyramids

All living things are in food chains (see Spread 2.24).

In a food chain, only a fraction of the energy taken in by one organism reaches the next. So fewer and fewer organisms can be fed at each stage. For example:

It might take 30 000 leaves to feed 300 snails, and 300 snails to feed one blackbird. This can be shown using a *pyramid of numbers* like the one below:

A leaf is lighter than a snail, which is lighter than a bird. So the *numbers* of leaves and snails do not tell you *how much* food is being eaten at each stage of the chain. For this, you need to know the total mass of each type of organism. This is called its *biomass*.

The biomasses of the leaves, snails, and bird have been worked out in the table below. Using this information, a *pyramid of biomass* can be drawn.

	a Number	*b* Mass of each in g	*a x b* Biomass in g
blackbirds	1	250	250
snails	300	50	15 000
leaves	30 000	20	600 000

(g = gram)

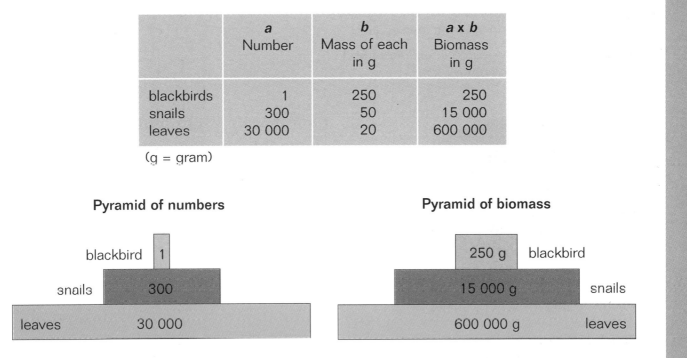

Pyramid of numbers

blackbird 1
snails 300
leaves 30 000

Pyramid of biomass

250 g blackbird
15 000 g snails
600 000 g leaves

---

1 Use the chart on the opposite page to estimate how much energy is stored in
  a 100 grams of bread
  b 100 grams of Cheddar cheese
  c 200 grams of crisps.

2 Crisps give you far more energy than boiled potatoes. Explain why it would *not* be a good idea to eat crisps with your meals instead of boiled potatoes.

3 What are *villi* and what do they do?

4 Where does digested food go after it has been absorbed in the small intestine?

5 A frog feeds on 250 worms. These feed on 25 000 leaves. Draw a pyramid of numbers for this.

6 The frog in the last question has a mass of 200 g, a worm 40 g, and a leaf 20 g. Draw a pyramid of biomass for this. (Hint: start by making a table like the one on this page.)

EXTENSION

Looking at matter

▶ **Mass**

Mass is the amount of matter in something. It can be measured in **kilograms (kg)**.

Small masses are measured in **grams (g)**.

1000 grams = 1 kilogram

To find the mass of something, you can weigh it.

mass = 53.2 g

▶ **Volume**

Volume is the amount of space something takes up. It can be measured in **cubic metres (m³)**.

Small volumes are measured in **millilitres (ml)**, also called **cubic centimetres (cm³)**.

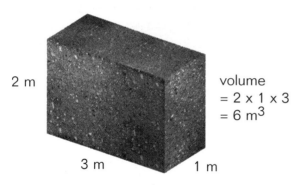

2 m

3 m 1 m

volume
= 2 x 1 x 3
= 6 m³

You can work out the volume of a block like this:

volume = length x width x height

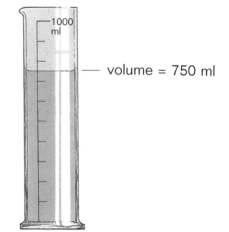
volume = 750 ml

You can find the volume of a liquid using a measuring cylinder.

▶ **Density**

Steel has a higher **density** than water - it has more kilograms in every cubic metre.

Density is measured in **kilograms per cubic metre (kg/m³)**:

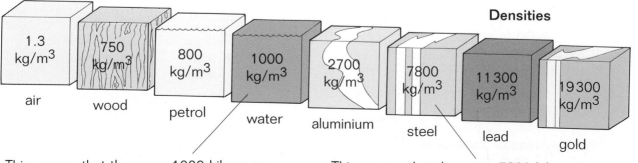

Densities

air	wood	petrol	water	aluminium	steel	lead	gold
1.3 kg/m³	750 kg/m³	800 kg/m³	1000 kg/m³	2700 kg/m³	7800 kg/m³	11 300 kg/m³	19 300 kg/m³

This means that there are 1000 kilograms in every cubic metre of water.

This means that there are 7800 kilograms in every cubic metre of steel.

Solid, liquid, or gas

Materials can be solid, liquid, or gas. These are their features:

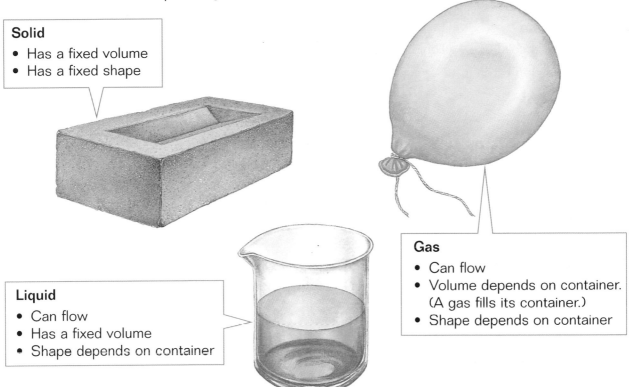

Solid
- Has a fixed volume
- Has a fixed shape

Gas
- Can flow
- Volume depends on container. (A gas fills its container.)
- Shape depends on container

Liquid
- Can flow
- Has a fixed volume
- Shape depends on container

Solids, liquids, and gases all have mass.
Gases are usually much lighter than liquids or solids.

1 Copy the table on the right. Put a tick (✔) or a cross (✗) in each box to show the different features of a solid, liquid, and gas.
For example, if you think a solid has a fixed volume, give that box a tick (✔). If you think a solid can't flow, give that box a cross (✗).

Feature ▼	Solid	Liquid	Gas
fixed shape			
fixed volume			
can flow			

2 Look at the density diagram on the left.
Write down the name (or names) of:
a a liquid that is less dense than water.
b two solids that are more dense than steel.
c a gas with a low density.
d a liquid which would have a mass of 2000 kg if you had 2 cubic metres of it.

3 *1   2   100   200   1000   2000*
Copy the following. Fill in the blanks, choosing from the numbers above.
a 1 kg = ____ g
b 2000 g = ____ kg

3.2 Hot and cold

▶ Changing state

Water can be a solid (ice), a liquid, or a gas (steam):

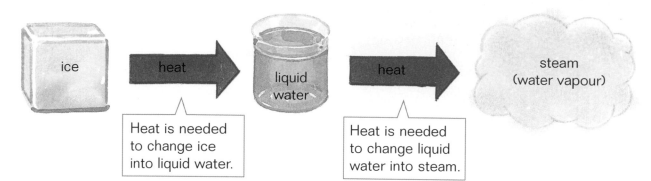

ice

heat

liquid water

heat

steam (water vapour)

Heat is needed to change ice into liquid water.

Heat is needed to change liquid water into steam.

A change from solid to liquid, liquid to gas, or back again is called a change of **state**.

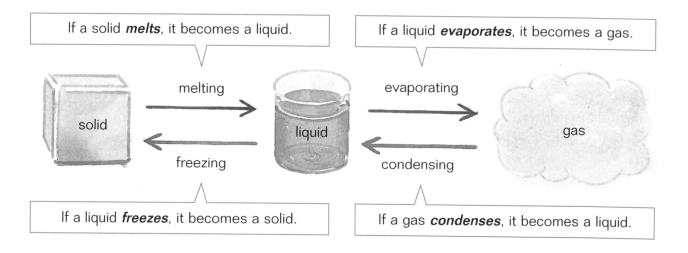

If a solid **melts**, it becomes a liquid.

If a liquid **evaporates**, it becomes a gas.

solid

melting →

← freezing

liquid

evaporating →

← condensing

gas

If a liquid **freezes**, it becomes a solid.

If a gas **condenses**, it becomes a liquid.

When water is cold, it evaporates very slowly.

When water is **boiling**, it bubbles, and evaporates very quickly.

The white cloud coming out of a kettle is steam which has condensed to form millions of tiny droplets. The real steam is invisible.

► Temperature

When something gets hotter, its *temperature* rises.

Temperature can be measured in *degrees Celsius* (*°C*) (sometimes called 'degrees centigrade').

On the Celsius scale, the numbers were specially chosen so that water freezes at 0 °C and boils at 100 °C.

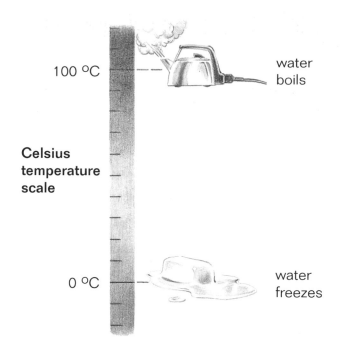

100 °C — water boils

Celsius temperature scale

0 °C — water freezes

► Expansion

If you heat a steel bar, it gets slightly bigger. It *expands* by a tiny amount. Most materials expand a little when heated.

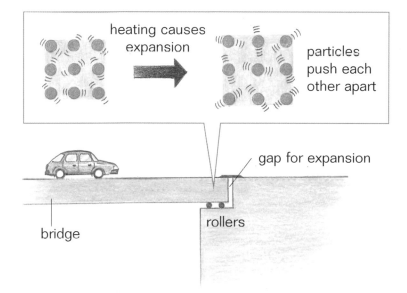

heating causes expansion

particles push each other apart

gap for expansion

bridge   rollers

Scientists think that all materials are made of tiny, moving particles, far too small to see with an ordinary microscope. Heating makes the particles move faster, so they push each other apart.

Gaps are left in bridges so that there is room for expansion on a hot day. Without a gap, the force of the expansion might crack the bridge.

---

1 Copy and complete these sentences:
   Water freezes at a temperature of....
   Water boils at a temperature of....

2 Copy these sentences. Fill in the blanks using the words on the right. (You can use the same word more than once):
   If a solid melts, it becomes a ____.
   If a liquid evaporates, it becomes a ____.
   If a liquid freezes, it becomes a ____.
   If a gas condenses, it becomes a ____.

> solid
>
> liquid
>
> gas

3 Explain why a bridge has a small gap left at the end.

Looking at materials

▶ **Properties of materials**

The features of a material and how it behaves are called its *properties*. Here are words for describing some properties:

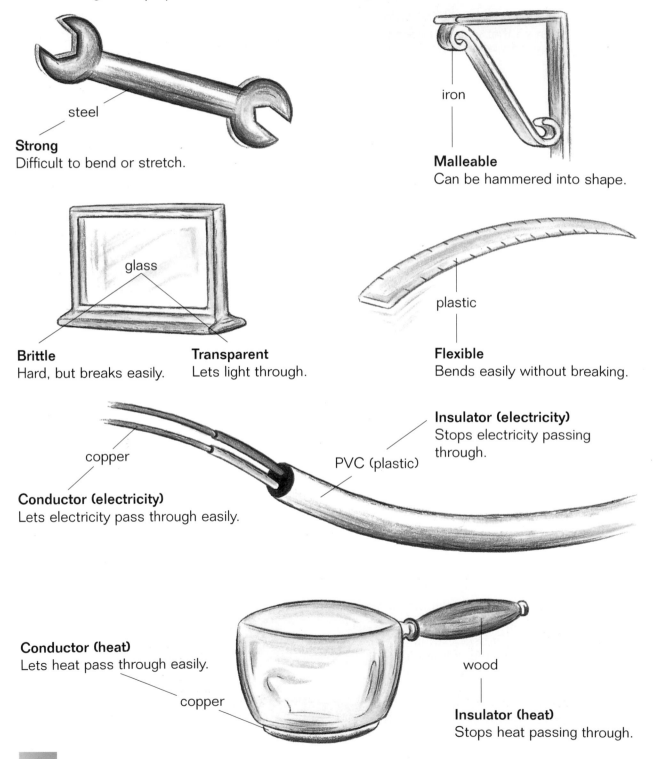

Strong
Difficult to bend or stretch.

steel

iron

Malleable
Can be hammered into shape.

glass

Brittle
Hard, but breaks easily.

Transparent
Lets light through.

plastic

Flexible
Bends easily without breaking.

copper

Conductor (electricity)
Lets electricity pass through easily.

PVC (plastic)

Insulator (electricity)
Stops electricity passing through.

Conductor (heat)
Lets heat pass through easily.

copper

wood

Insulator (heat)
Stops heat passing through.

▶ Useful materials

Here are five types of materials used for making things.
The properties are the ones they *usually* have.

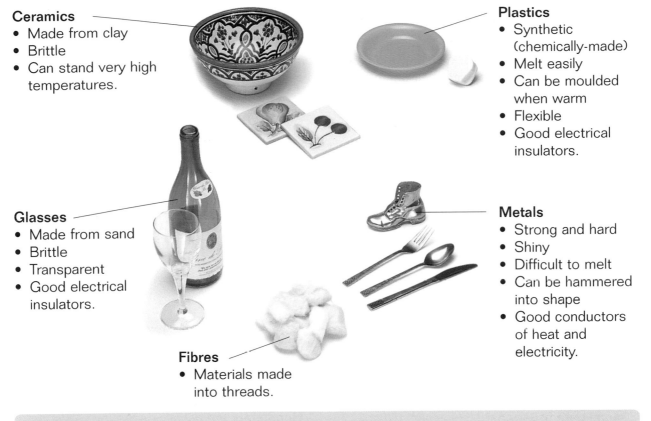

Ceramics
- Made from clay
- Brittle
- Can stand very high temperatures.

Plastics
- Synthetic (chemically-made)
- Melt easily
- Can be moulded when warm
- Flexible
- Good electrical insulators.

Glasses
- Made from sand
- Brittle
- Transparent
- Good electrical insulators.

Metals
- Strong and hard
- Shiny
- Difficult to melt
- Can be hammered into shape
- Good conductors of heat and electricity.

Fibres
- Materials made into threads.

1 *brittle   malleable   flexible   transparent   strong*

   Write down a word for each of these, choosing from the words above:
   a Hard, but breaks easily.
   b Bends easily without breaking.
   c Lets light through.
   d Can be hammered into shape.

2 Copy the table on the right. Fill in the blanks by writing in a material with each property. (The first one has been done for you.)

3 *heat insulator   electrical insulator   transparent flexible   strong*

   Choosing from the words above, write down the properties that a material should have for each of these jobs. (You can choose the same words more than once.)
   a Tow rope.
   b Table mat.
   c Cover of an electric plug.
   d Sides of a fish tank.

Property	Material
transparent	glass
flexible	
brittle	
conductor (heat)	
conductor (electricity)	
insulator (heat)	
insulator (electricity)	

3.4 Elements, atoms, and compounds

▶ **Elements**

Everything on Earth is made from about 90 simple substances called **elements**.

There are two main types of element: **metals** and **nonmetals**. Here are some examples, with their chemical symbols:

Metals	
Element	*Symbol*
aluminium	Al
calcium	Ca
copper	Cu
gold	Au
iron	Fe
lead	Pb
magnesium	Mg
potassium	K
silver	Ag
sodium	Na
tin	Sn
zinc	Zn

Nonmetals	
Element	*Symbol*
bromine	Br
carbon	C
chlorine	Cl
fluorine	F
helium	He
hydrogen	H
iodine	I
nitrogen	N
oxygen	O
phosphorus	P
silicon	Si
sulphur	S

Metals are usually hard, shiny, and difficult to melt. They are good conductors of heat and electricity. (For more on metals, see spreads 3.3 and 3.10.)

Examples

Copper

Aluminium

Nonmetals are usually gases, or solids which melt easily. The solids are often brittle or powdery. Most nonmetals are insulators - though carbon is a good conductor of electricity.

Examples

Sulphur　　　**Carbon**

▶ **Atoms**

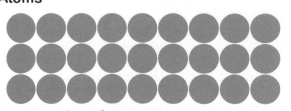

atoms in a bar of copper

The smallest bit of an element is called an **atom**. Each element has its own type of atom.

Atoms are very, very small. It would take more than a billion billion atoms to cover this dot!

▶ Compounds

Atoms can join together to form new substances, called *compounds*. These may be nothing like the elements in them.

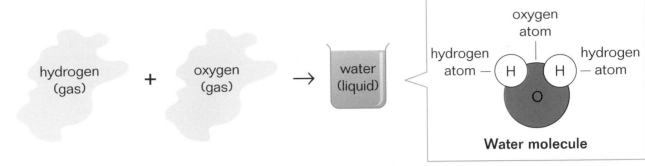

Water molecule

Water is a compound of hydrogen and oxygen. It is made when hydrogen burns in oxygen. But it is nothing like either of these.

The smallest bit of water is called a *molecule* of water. It is made of two hydrogen atoms stuck to one oxygen atom.

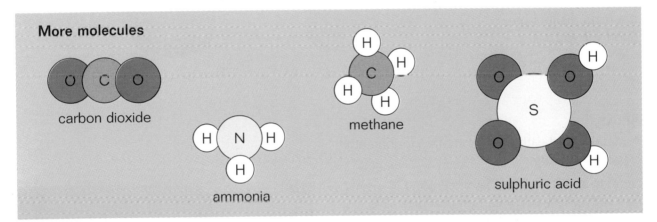

More molecules

carbon dioxide

ammonia

methane

sulphuric acid

Atoms don't really have colours. The colours here are to help you tell the atoms apart.

1 *nonmetals   metals   atoms   compounds   elements*
   Copy these sentences. Fill in the blanks, choosing words from those above. You can use the same word more than once.
   _____ are usually hard and shiny.
   _____ are the smallest bits of elements.
   _____ are good conductors of heat and electricity.
   _____ are usually insulators.
   _____ are made from more than one element.

2 Write down the names of the elements with these symbols:
   H   O   C   N   S

3 Copy the table on the right. Fill in the blanks by writing in the elements in each compound. The first one has been done for you.

Compound	Elements
ammonia	nitrogen hydrogen
water	
carbon dioxide	
sulphuric acid	

Mixtures and solutions

▶ Mixtures

One substance by itself is called a *pure* substance.

Most substances are not like this. They have other things mixed in. They are *mixtures*.

Mineral water may not be pure, but this does not mean it is dirty. Many of the minerals in it are good for you.

Distilled water
Contains: water

This is pure

Mineral water
Contains: water
+ small amounts of
bicarbonates
calcium
chlorides
sodium
magnesium
potassium
silica
sulphates
nitrates

This is a mixture

▶ Alloys

A metal mixed with another metal (or nonmetal) is called an *alloy*.

Steel is an alloy of iron and carbon. It is mainly iron with a little bit of carbon mixed in. This makes it harder and stronger than iron by itself.

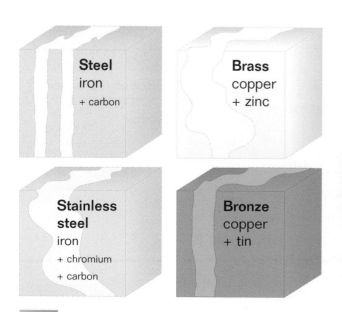

Steel
iron
+ carbon

Brass
copper
+ zinc

Stainless steel
iron
+ chromium
+ carbon

Bronze
copper
+ tin

Brass is an alloy of copper and zinc. Unlike pure copper, it keeps its shine and colour.

▶ Solutions

If you put sugar in water, the sugar breaks up into tiny bits
which float away. The bits are so small that you cannot see
them even with a microscope.

The sugar has **dissolved** in the water.
Scientists say that sugar is **soluble** in water.
The mixture of sugar and water is called a **solution**:

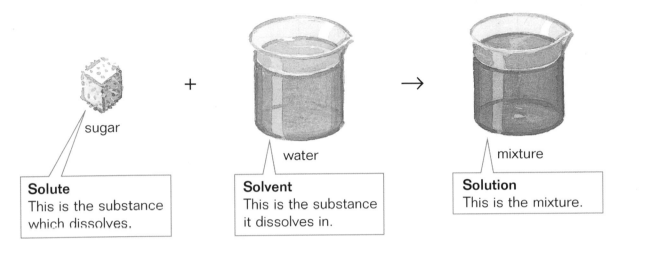

sugar + water → mixture

Solute
This is the substance
which dissolves.

Solvent
This is the substance
it dissolves in.

Solution
This is the mixture.

Water is not the only solvent. Here are some others:

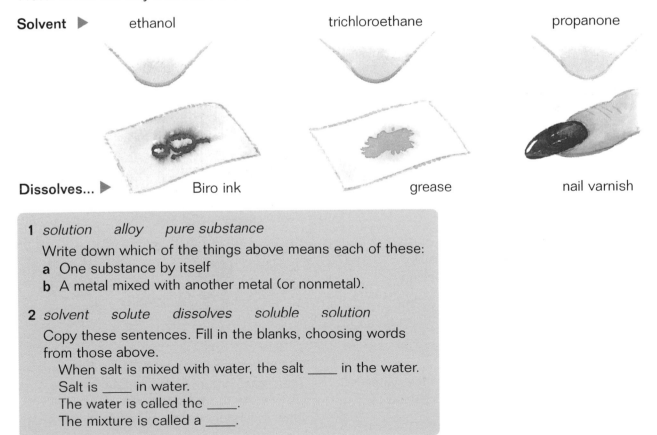

| Solvent ▶ | ethanol | trichloroethane | propanone |
| Dissolves... ▶ | Biro ink | grease | nail varnish |

1 *solution   alloy   pure substance*
   Write down which of the things above means each of these:
   a One substance by itself
   b A metal mixed with another metal (or nonmetal).

2 *solvent   solute   dissolves   soluble   solution*
   Copy these sentences. Fill in the blanks, choosing words
   from those above.
       When salt is mixed with water, the salt ____ in the water.
       Salt is ____ in water.
       The water is called the ____.
       The mixture is called a ____.

Separating mixtures

Here are some methods of separating mixtures in the laboratory:

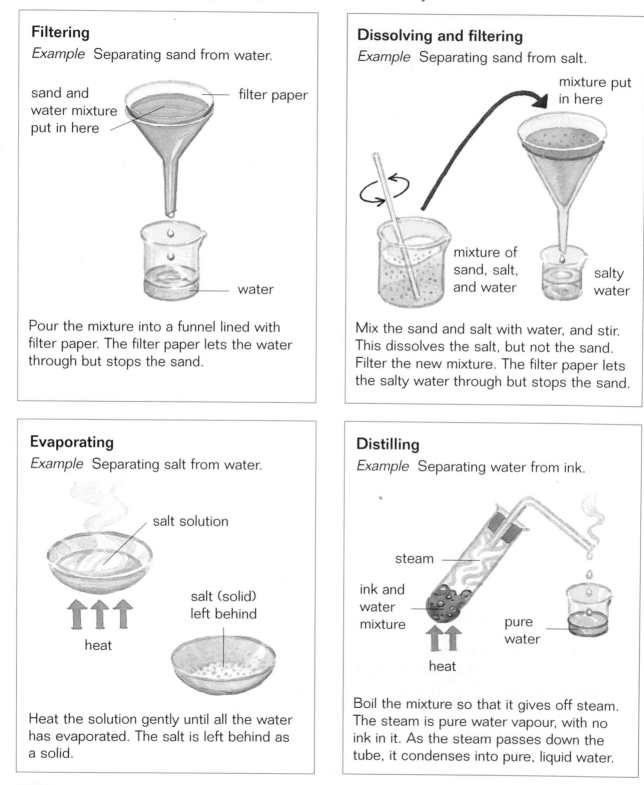

Filtering

Example Separating sand from water.

sand and water mixture put in here

filter paper

water

Pour the mixture into a funnel lined with filter paper. The filter paper lets the water through but stops the sand.

Dissolving and filtering

Example Separating sand from salt.

mixture put in here

mixture of sand, salt, and water

salty water

Mix the sand and salt with water, and stir. This dissolves the salt, but not the sand. Filter the new mixture. The filter paper lets the salty water through but stops the sand.

Evaporating

Example Separating salt from water.

salt solution

salt (solid) left behind

heat

Heat the solution gently until all the water has evaporated. The salt is left behind as a solid.

Distilling

Example Separating water from ink.

steam

ink and water mixture

pure water

heat

Boil the mixture so that it gives off steam. The steam is pure water vapour, with no ink in it. As the steam passes down the tube, it condenses into pure, liquid water.

Crystallizing

Example Separating copper sulphate from water.

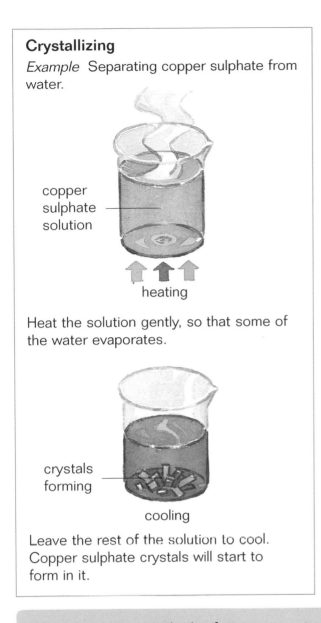

copper sulphate solution

heating

Heat the solution gently, so that some of the water evaporates.

crystals forming

cooling

Leave the rest of the solution to cool. Copper sulphate crystals will start to form in it.

Chromatography

Example Separating inks of different colours.

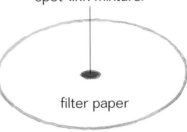

spot (ink mixture)

filter paper

Put a spot of ink mixture in the middle of a piece of filter paper and leave it to dry.

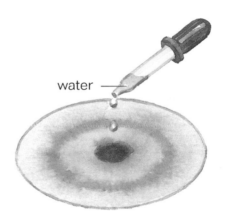

water

Drip water onto the spot. The ink mixture spreads through the damp paper. The different colours spread at different rates.

---

1 Here are some methods of separating mixtures:
   *filtering   evaporating   crystallizing   distilling
   dissolving and filtering   chromatography*

   Write down which method you would use for each of these jobs (the information on the right may help):
   a Separating sand and salt.
   b Separating sand and sugar.
   c Separating mud and water.
   d Separating water paints of different colours.

2 A tea-bag is a filter. Write down what things you think it separates.

3 The bag in a vacuum cleaner is a filter. Write down what things you think it separates.

> Mud is tiny bits of soil floating in water
>
> Sugar will dissolve in water

3.7 Acids and alkalis

▶ **Acids**

There are acids in the laboratory. But there are natural acids in vinegar, sour fruits, and even in your stomach!

Acids dissolved in lots of water are called *dilute* acids. Acids dissolved in only a little water are *concentrated* acids.

When dissolved in water, acids are *corrosive* . They eat into materials such as carbonates and some metals.

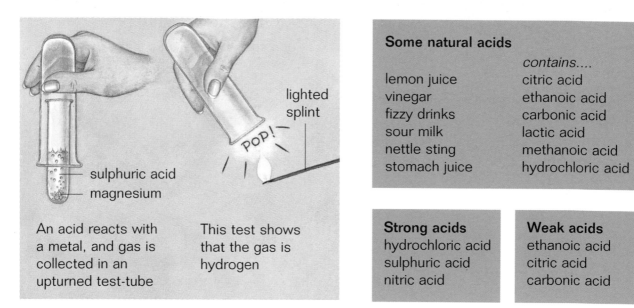

lighted splint

POP!

sulphuric acid
magnesium

An acid reacts with a metal, and gas is collected in an upturned test-tube

This test shows that the gas is hydrogen

Some natural acids

	contains....
lemon juice	citric acid
vinegar	ethanoic acid
fizzy drinks	carbonic acid
sour milk	lactic acid
nettle sting	methanoic acid
stomach juice	hydrochloric acid

Strong acids
hydrochloric acid
sulphuric acid
nitric acid

Weak acids
ethanoic acid
citric acid
carbonic acid

All acids contain hydrogen. When an acid eats into a metal, the hydrogen is released as a gas.

Acids which act quickly, and release lots of hydrogen, are called *strong acids*. Acids which act slowly are *weak acids*.

▶ **Alkalis**

Alkalis are chemicals which can *neutralize* acids. They can cancel out their acid effect (see the next page).

Strong alkalis
sodium hydroxide
potassium hydroxide
calcium hydroxide

Weak alkali
ammonia

Alkalis can be just as corrosive as acids. Their powerful chemical action is often used in bath, sink, and oven cleaners, like those in the picture.

▶ Neutralization

Neutralizing acids is called *neutralization*. Here are two examples:

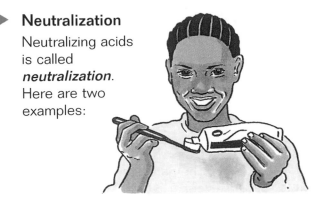

Sugar in your mouth produces acids which rot your teeth. Toothpaste is alkaline. It neutralizes these acids.

Acid in your stomach can become a bit too concentrated. Indigestion tablets release an alkali which neutralizes some of the acid.

▶ Testing for acids and alkalis

You can use *litmus paper* to test for an acid or alkali:

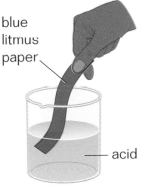

blue litmus paper

— acid

Acids turn blue litmus paper red.

— neutral

If a solution is *neutral* (neither acid nor alkaline), the paper doesn't change colour.

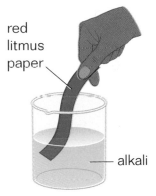

red litmus paper

— alkali

Alkalis turn red litmus paper blue.

---

1 Copy the table on the right. Fill in the blanks, by writing 'acid' or 'alkali' in each space. The first one has been done for you.

2 Copy and complete these sentences:
   a An acid dissolved in lots of water is called a .... acid.
   b An acid dissolved in only a little water is called a .... acid.
   c If an acid eats into a metal, ... is released.
   d If an alkali *neutralizes* an acid, this means that........
   e If you dip litmus paper into a neutral solution, the paper........

	acid or alkali
Sour milk	acid
Turns blue litmus paper red	
Turns red litmus paper blue	
Always contains hydrogen	
Toothpaste	
Lemon juice	
Indigestion tablets	
Oven cleaner	
Vinegar	
Ammonia	

3.8 Particles and atoms

▶ Solids, liquids, and gases

Solids, liquids, and gases are made up of tiny, moving particles. These particles attract each other.

Solid
The particles are very close together. They vibrate, but cannot change positions because the attractions are too strong.

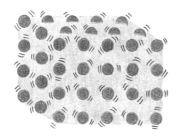

A solid has a fixed volume and a fixed shape.

Reason The particles are very close together and can't change positions

Liquid
The particles are close together. They vibrate, but can change positions because the attractions are not so strong.

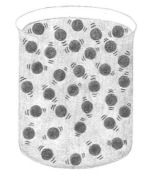

A liquid has a fixed volume, but can flow and change shape.

Reason The particles are close together, but can change positions.

Gas
The particles are spaced out. They can move about freely at high speed because the attractions are very weak.

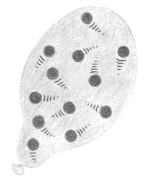

A gas fills its container, and can be compressed

Reason The particles can move about, and are spaced out.

In some substances the particles are atoms. In others they are groups of atoms, called **molecules** (see Spread 3.4).

water molecule

cold water   hot water   water vapour (steam)

When the temperature of water rises, the molecules vibrate faster.

When the molecules are vibrating fast enough, they break free from each other and form a gas (see Spread 3.2).

Dissolving...

When a solid *dissolves* in a liquid, its particles gradually mix with those in the liquid. (The liquid is the solvent: see Spread 3.5.)

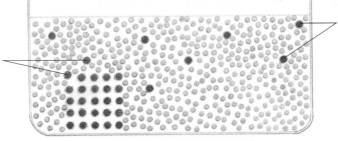

...and diffusion

The particles slowly spread as they are bumped into by other particles around them. This is called *diffusion*. Gases also spread by diffusion.

▶ Inside atoms

Atoms are made up of smaller particles, called *protons*, *neutrons*, and *electrons*. Atoms of different elements (see Spread 3.4) have different numbers of particles in them.

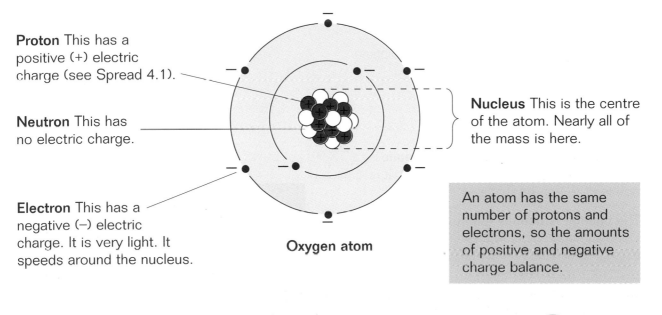

Proton This has a positive (+) electric charge (see Spread 4.1).

Neutron This has no electric charge.

Electron This has a negative (−) electric charge. It is very light. It speeds around the nucleus.

Oxygen atom

Nucleus This is the centre of the atom. Nearly all of the mass is here.

An atom has the same number of protons and electrons, so the amounts of positive and negative charge balance.

1 Write down whether each of these statements describes a *solid*, a *liquid*, or a *gas*:
   a Spaced-out particles which shoot about freely.
   b Vibrating particles which can change positions.
   c Vibrating particles which cannot change positions.

2 Look at the diagrams of the atoms above and on the right. Then copy and complete these sentences:
   The centre of an atom is called its ___.
   The particles in the nucleus are called ___ and ___.
   The particles speeding around the nucleus are called ___.
   An oxygen atom has eight protons and ___ electrons.
   A helium atom has ___ protons and ___ electrons.

Hydrogen atom

Helium atom

Changing materials

▶ Chemical change

When iron and sulphur are mixed and heated, they join to make a completely new substance, iron sulphide.

heat
→

iron (metal)   sulphur (yellow powder)   iron sulphide (black solid)

This is an example of a *chemical change*. Iron has *reacted* with sulphur. There has been a *chemical reaction* between the two. Here is a *word equation* for the reaction:

iron   +   sulphur   →   iron sulphide

▶ Signs of chemical change

If there is a chemical change:

One or more new substances are made
Iron sulphide is a compound (see 3.4). It is nothing like iron or sulphur.

The change is usually difficult to reverse
Changing iron sulphide back into iron and sulphur is difficult. Several reactions are needed.

Energy is given out or taken in
When iron reacts with sulphur, heat is given out.

Here are some examples of chemical change:

Once you have cooked eggs, you can't change them back again.

These chemical reactions give out energy as heat and light.

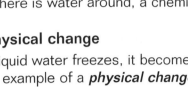

$+$ oxygen (in air) $\rightarrow$

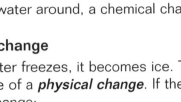

iron

rust (iron oxide)

If there is water around, a chemical change turns these..... ......into this.

► Physical change

If liquid water freezes, it becomes ice. This is an example of a **physical change**. If there is a physical change:

No new substances are made
Ice is still water, even though it is a solid.

The change is usually easy to reverse
Ice can melt to form liquid water again.

Here are some examples of physical change:

Liquid water can change into steam. When steam condenses, it becomes liquid water again.

Salt dissolves in water. But if you evaporate the water, you are left with the salt again.

---

1 *physical   chemical*

Copy these sentences. Fill in the blanks, choosing words from those above. (You can use the same word more than once.)

a In a ____ change, one or more new substances are made.

b A ____ change is usually difficult to reverse.

c In a ____ change, you end up with the same substance that you started with.

2 Copy the table on the right. Fill in the blanks, by writing 'physical' or 'chemical' in each space. The first one has been done for you.

	Change: physical or chemical
Cooking an egg	chemical
Ice melting	
Salt dissolving in water	
Baking a cake	
Iron going rusty	
Hot fat going solid when cooled	
Wood burning	

3.10 Burning

▶ Combustion

Combustion is another word for burning. It happens when substances react with oxygen in the air. When things burn, they give out energy as heat and light.

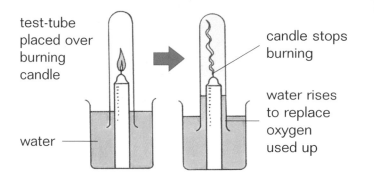

test-tube placed over burning candle

candle stops burning

water rises to replace oxygen used up

water

This experiment shows that about 1/5 of the air is used up when something burns. That is because about 1/5 of the air is oxygen.

Combustion

▶ Burning fuels

Petrol, coal, wood, and natural gas (methane) are all *fuels*.

Most fuels are compounds of hydrogen and carbon. When they burn, they make carbon dioxide and water, as on the right.

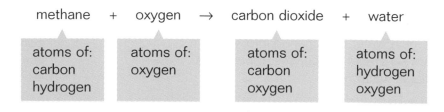

methane + oxygen → carbon dioxide + water

| atoms of: carbon hydrogen | atoms of: oxygen | atoms of: carbon oxygen | atoms of: hydrogen oxygen |

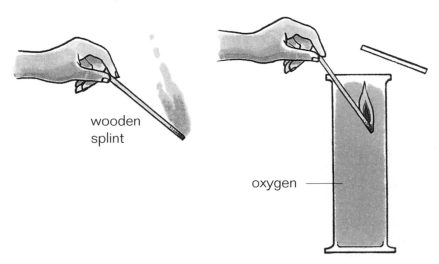

wooden splint

oxygen

Testing for oxygen Fuels burn more fiercely in pure oxygen than in air. You can use this fact to test for oxygen:

If a glowing wooden splint is put into oxygen, the splint will burst into flames.

▶ Fire!

The **combustion triangle** below shows the three things needed for burning. Getting rid of any of them stops the burning. So firefighters have three ways of putting out a fire.

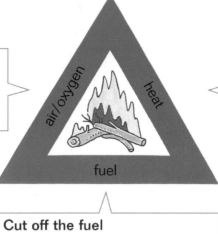

Cut off the air supply
For example Use a fire blanket, foam, or carbon dioxide gas.

Get rid of the heat
For example Cool things down with water.

Note Water is not safe for some fires. It conducts electricity and can give people shocks. Also, it can make burning fat or oil splatter and spread.

Cut off the fuel
For example Turn off the gas at the mains.

air/oxygen

heat

fuel

▶ Burning food

To get energy, your body 'burns up' food slowly, without any flames. This is called **respiration** (see 2.2). It makes carbon dioxide and water:

food + oxygen → carbon dioxide + water

▶ Testing for carbon dioxide

Carbon dioxide turns **limewater** milky. You can use this fact to tell that there is carbon dioxide in the air you breathe out.

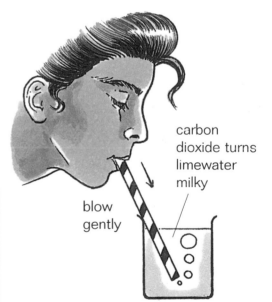

blow gently

carbon dioxide turns limewater milky

1 Here are three gases:
 oxygen   carbon dioxide   methane
 Write down which gas does each of these.
 (You can choose the same gas more than once.)
 a Puts out fires.
 b Is needed for burning.
 c Is made when most fuels burn.
 d Is used as a fuel.
 e Makes a glowing splint burst into flames.
 f Is made when your body 'burns up' food.
 g Turns limewater milky.

2 Write down the *three* things needed for burning.

3.11 More chemical reactions

▶ **Rearranging atoms**

In chemical reactions, atoms get rearranged to make new substances. For example:

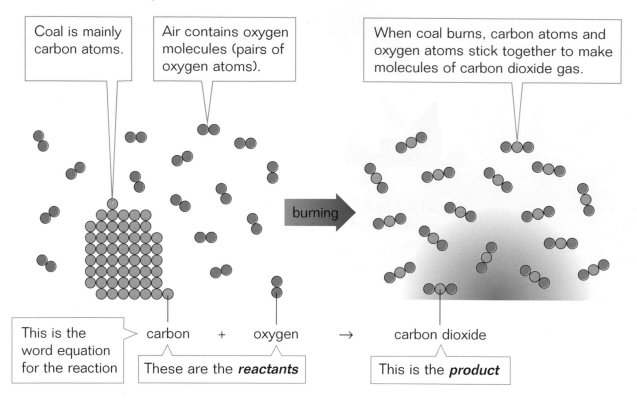

Coal is mainly carbon atoms.

Air contains oxygen molecules (pairs of oxygen atoms).

When coal burns, carbon atoms and oxygen atoms stick together to make molecules of carbon dioxide gas.

burning

This is the word equation for the reaction

These are the *reactants*

This is the *product*

carbon   +   oxygen   →   carbon dioxide

Making water

When hydrogen burns in oxygen, water is made. This is how the atoms get rearranged to make water molecules:

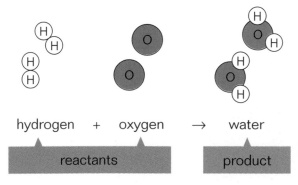

hydrogen   +   oxygen   →   water

reactants   product

Each molecule of water is made from two atoms of hydrogen and one atom of oxygen. That is why water is called 'H_2O'.

Burning coal. The yellow in the flame is light from tiny, glowing particles of carbon.

Acid-metal reactions

Most metals react with acids. For example, if magnesium is put into sulphuric acid, there is this reaction:

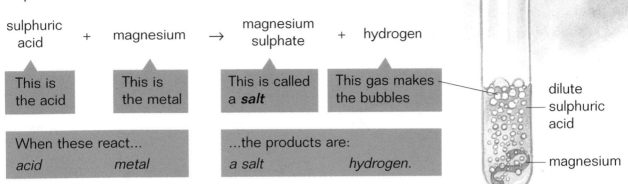

sulphuric acid + magnesium → magnesium sulphate + hydrogen

| This is the acid | This is the metal | This is called a **salt** | This gas makes the bubbles |

| When these react... | ...the products are: |
| acid   metal | a salt   hydrogen. |

dilute sulphuric acid

magnesium

There are lots of different types of salt.

Acid-carbonate reactions

Carbonates react with acids. For example, if limestone (calcium carbonate) is put into hydrochloric acid, there is this reaction:

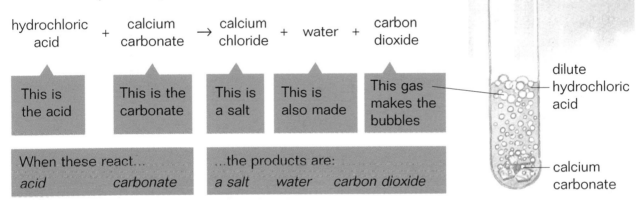

hydrochloric acid + calcium carbonate → calcium chloride + water + carbon dioxide

| This is the acid | This is the carbonate | This is a salt | This is also made | This gas makes the bubbles |

| When these react... | ...the products are: |
| acid   carbonate | a salt   water   carbon dioxide |

dilute hydrochloric acid

calcium carbonate

Limestone rock is attacked by the acid in rain (see Spread 3.20).

1 *carbon dioxide   water   hydrogen*
   There are three substances above. Write down the one which goes with each of the following:
   a This is made when hydrogen burns in oxygen.
   b This gas is made when an acid reacts with a metal.
   c This gas is made when an acid reacts with a carbonate.

2 Here is chemical reaction between an acid and a metal:
   sulphuric acid + zinc → zinc sulphate + hydrogen
   a Write down the substances which are the reactants.
   b Write down the substances which are the products.
   c Write down the substance which is a salt.

3.12 More about metals

▶ **Corrosion**

The surface of a metal may be attacked by air, water, or other substances around it. This is called **corrosion**. Iron corrodes by going rusty. Steel is mainly iron. It can also go rusty.

The experiment on the right shows that air *and* water are needed for rusting. Dry air has no effect. Nor does water, if it has no air in it.

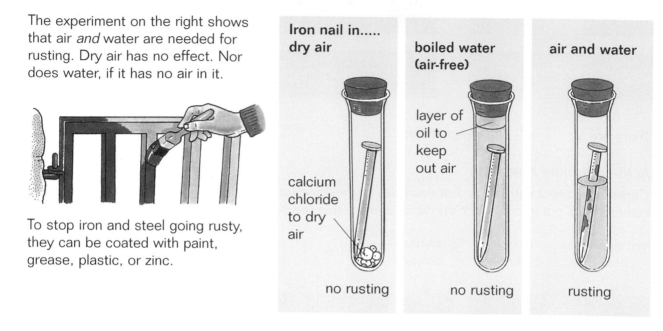

Iron nail in.....
dry air

boiled water (air-free)

air and water

layer of oil to keep out air

calcium chloride to dry air

no rusting   no rusting   rusting

To stop iron and steel going rusty, they can be coated with paint, grease, plastic, or zinc.

▶ **Reactive and unreactive**

Iron is a **reactive** metal. It reacts with other elements to form compounds. For example, it reacts with oxygen in the air to form rust.

Gold is an **unreactive** metal. It does not react with oxygen or acids. So it does not corrode however long it is left in the air or soil.

▶ Where metals come from

Most of our metals come from rocks in the ground. They are in compounds called **ores**. The metal has to be separated from its ore using heat or electricity.

Unreactive metals, such as gold, are found in the ground as small bits of the metal itself.

	Aluminium	Copper	Iron	Gold
Metal				
Useful properties	Light and strong, good conductor of electricity and heat	Very good conductor of electricity and heat	Can be made into steel, which is very strong	Doesn't corrode
Where found	In ore called bauxite	In ores such as cuprite	In ore called haematite	In rock, as a metal

To make steel, a tiny amount of carbon is added to pure, *molten* iron ('molten' means 'melted'). Steel is an **alloy** of iron and carbon. For more on alloys, see Spread 3.5.

1 Here are four metals:
   copper   aluminium   gold   iron
   Copy the following sentences. Fill in the blanks, choosing words from those above. (You can use the same word more than once.)
   a ____ is light and strong.
   b ____ is a very good conductor of electricity.
   c ____ is a very good conductor of heat.
   d ____ does not corrode.
   e ____ corrodes by going rusty.
   f ____ can be made into steel.
   g ____ is unreactive.
   h ____ is found in the ground as a metal, not an ore.

2 Write down *two* things which are needed for iron or steel to go rusty.

3 Write down *two* ways of stopping iron or steel going rusty.

Iron and steel

▶ Producing iron

Iron ore is mainly a compound of iron and oxygen. To get the iron out, the oxygen has to be removed. This is done in a **blast furnace**, using heat and chemical reactions. It is called **smelting**.

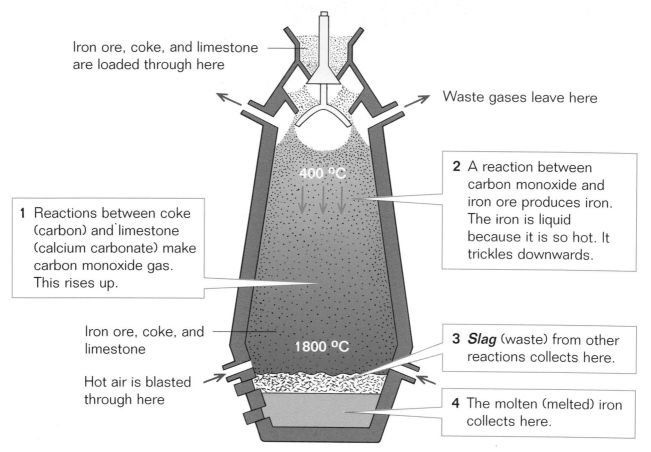

Iron ore, coke, and limestone are loaded through here

Waste gases leave here

400 °C

2 A reaction between carbon monoxide and iron ore produces iron. The iron is liquid because it is so hot. It trickles downwards.

1 Reactions between coke (carbon) and limestone (calcium carbonate) make carbon monoxide gas. This rises up.

Iron ore, coke, and limestone

Hot air is blasted through here

1800 °C

3 *Slag* (waste) from other reactions collects here.

4 The molten (melted) iron collects here.

Blast furnace

Iron from a blast furnace is called **pig iron**. It has impurities in it, including carbon (about 4%). This makes it brittle.

Most pig iron is made into steel.

Crushed slag is used in road building, in the foundations.

The photograph on the right shows molten (melted) iron draining from a blast furnace.

Producing steel

These are the main stages in producing steel:

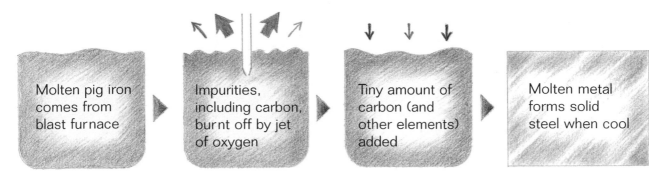

Molten pig iron comes from blast furnace	Impurities, including carbon, burnt off by jet of oxygen	Tiny amount of carbon (and other elements) added	Molten metal forms solid steel when cool

A tiny amount of carbon (1% or less) makes steel hard but not brittle.

Using iron and steel

Here are some different types of iron and steel, and some of the things they are used for:

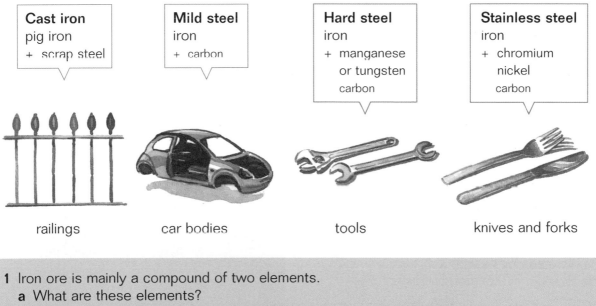

Cast iron
pig iron
+ scrap steel

Mild steel
iron
+ carbon

Hard steel
iron
+ manganese
  or tungsten
  carbon

Stainless steel
iron
+ chromium
  nickel
  carbon

railings   car bodies   tools   knives and forks

---

1 Iron ore is mainly a compound of two elements.
   a What are these elements?
   b What piece of equipment is used to separate them?

2 Copy these in the correct order to show how steel is made:
   Molten metal cools and turns solid.
   Molten pig iron comes from a blast furnace.
   Tiny amounts of carbon and other elements are added.
   Impurities are burnt off by a jet of oxygen.

   > mild steel
   > hard steel
   > stainless steel
   > pig iron

3 Look at the list of four metals on the right.
   a Write down *two* elements which are in all these metals.
   b Write down *two* elements which are only in stainless steel.
   c Write down *two* uses of pig iron.

Limestone

Limestone is a common rock. It is mainly calcium carbonate. It formed from the shells and bones of ancient sea creatures.

Industry needs millions of tonnes of limestone every year. The limestone comes from huge quarries. But these spoil the countryside.

Here are some of the uses of limestone:

▶ Making cement

Cement is a grey powder. When mixed with water, it sets hard.

Cement is made like this, using limestone and clay:

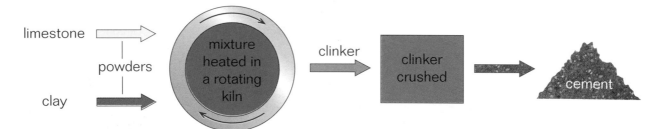

▶ Making glass

Glass is made by heating a mixture of sand, soda (sodium carbonate), and limestone.

Molten (melted) glass is soft. It can be moulded or blown into different shapes. ▶

▶ Making iron and steel

Steel is made from iron. Iron is produced in a blast furnace (see Spread 3.13). Limestone is needed for some of the chemical reactions in the blast furnace.

▶ Chippings for the building industry

Chippings These are usually tiny bits of limestone.

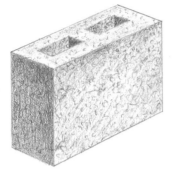

Concrete This is made by mixing chippings, sand, cement, and water.

Tarmac This is made from chippings coated with tar.

▶ Making soils less acid

Some soils are too acid for crops to grow. To neutralize the acid, farmers can put one of these white powders on the soil:

Chalk (calcium carbonate) This is a soft, white, crumbly form of limestone.

Quicklime (calcium oxide) This is made by heating limestone strongly.

Slaked lime (calcium hydroxide) This is made by adding water to quicklime.

---

1 Copy and complete this sentence:
   Industry gets its limestone from...

2 Choose the word on the right which goes with each of these:
   a Broken-up bits of limestone.
   b Made with chippings, sand, cement, and water.
   c Made using limestone and clay.
   d Put on soil to make it less acid.
   e Made using sand, soda, and limestone.

   > glass
   > chippings
   > concrete
   > cement
   > quicklime

3 Write down *two* ways in which limestone is used in the making of concrete.

3.15 Oil and plastics

▶ ## Oil

Oil companies get their oil from the ground (see Spread 4.18). They call it **crude oil**.

Crude oil is a mixture of substances called **hydrocarbons**. Their molecules are made from atoms of hydrogen and carbon. ▶

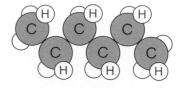

The different substances in crude oil are called **fractions**. At the refinery, they are separated in a **fractionating tower**.

The oil is boiled. Its vapour rises up the tower. As the vapour rises, it cools. Different fractions condense (turn liquid) at different temperatures. They collect in trays at different levels.

Separating substances by boiling is called **distillation**.

cool (25 °C)

hot crude oil →

hot steam to heat oil →

hot (450 °C)

refinery gas → methane → bottled gas

petrol

kerosene → jet fuel → paraffin

diesel oil → diesel fuel → heating oil

heavy oils → engine oils → grease → waxes

residue → tar

▶ ## Changing molecules from oil

Heavy fractions (such as heavy oils) have long molecules.

Fractions can be changed like this.

Light fractions (such as petrol) have short molecules.

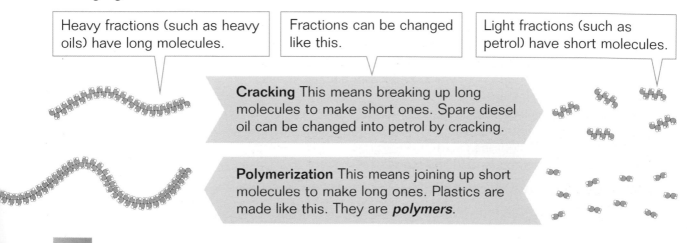

Cracking This means breaking up long molecules to make short ones. Spare diesel oil can be changed into petrol by cracking.

Polymerization This means joining up short molecules to make long ones. Plastics are made like this. They are **polymers**.

Made from oil

In a chemical works, oil fractions can be used to make new materials. To do this, other chemicals may be needed as well.

Here are some of the materials made using oil:

Plastics

PVC

polythene

polystyrene

polypropene

Other materials

white spirit

polishes

detergents

synthetic rubber

other solvents   chemicals

---

1 Choose the word on the right which goes with each of these:
   a Its molecules are made from atoms of hydrogen and carbon.
   b The different substances in crude oil are separated in this.
   c Joining up short molecules to make long ones.
   d Separating substances by boiling.
   e Breaking up long molecules to make short ones.

2 Write down the names of *two* fuels that come from crude oil.

3 Write down the names of *two* plastics that are made using oil.

4 Write down the names of *two* other materials that are made using oil.

> cracking
> hydrocarbon
> polymerization
> condensing
> fractionating tower
> distillation

Air is not one gas. It is a mixture of gases.
The pie chart shows the main gases in air.

Oxygen

- Animals and plants need oxygen to stay alive.
- Oxygen is needed to make things burn.
- Oxygen affects some foods and makes them go off.

Carbon dioxide and other gases

- These are just a tiny fraction of the air. There is more about them on the next page.

Nitrogen

- Nitrates have nitrogen in them. Plants need nitrates for healthy growth.
- Nitrogen is combined with hydrogen to make ammonia. Ammonia is needed to make plastics, and fertilizers for farmers.
- Nitrogen helps preserve food in packets. Nitrogen doesn't make food go off.

- Very cold, liquid nitrogen is used for freezing food quickly.

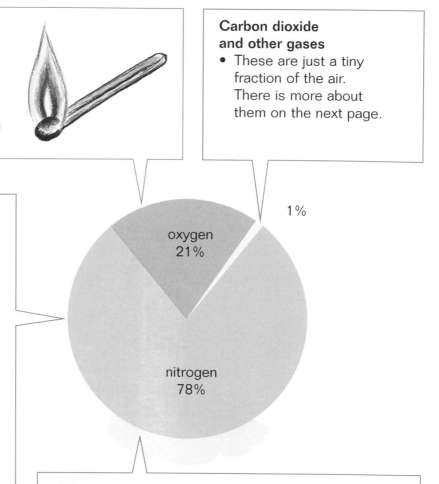

oxygen 21%

1%

nitrogen 78%

Water vapour

- Damp air has some water vapour in it. When water vapour condenses into millions of tiny drops, we see these as clouds and fog.

Carbon dioxide....

- Plants take in carbon dioxide for growth.

- Some fire extinguishers shoot out carbon dioxide. Things can't burn in carbon dioxide.

- Carbon dioxide is the gas that puts the fizz in fizzy drinks.

- Solid carbon dioxide is called 'dry ice'. It is much colder than ordinary ice. It is used for storing frozen fish and other foods.

...and other gases

- Argon is used to fill light bulbs. It stops the filament burning up.

- Helium is lighter than other gases in air. It is used to fill balloons.

- Neon is used in lamps that give a red glow.

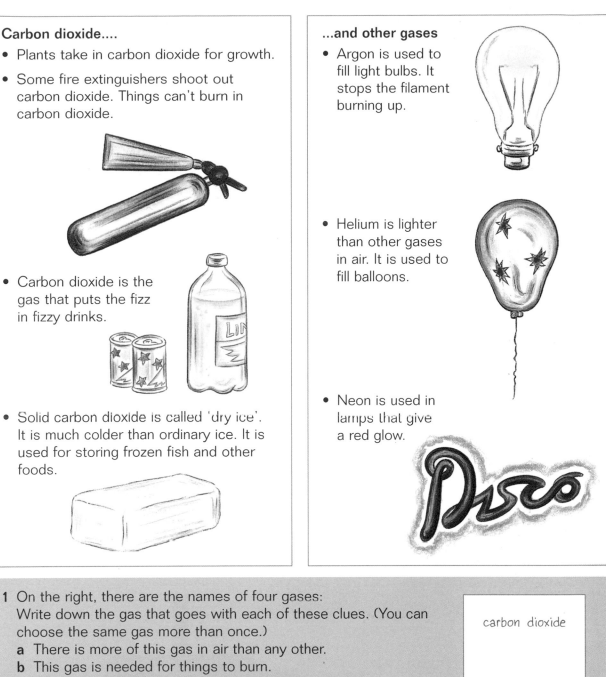

1 On the right, there are the names of four gases:
   Write down the gas that goes with each of these clues. (You can choose the same gas more than once.)
   a There is more of this gas in air than any other.
   b This gas is needed for things to burn.
   c When this gas freezes, it becomes 'dry ice'.
   d This gas is needed to make nitrates for plants.

2 Copy and complete these sentences. You must start each sentence with one of the gases on the right, then finish it with your own words:
   a _____ is used to fill balloons because.....
   b _____ is used in fire extinguishers because.....
   c _____ is used to fill crisp packets because.....

3 The gases on the right are all part of the air. Write down the name of *one* other gas in air. Describe what it is used for.

carbon dioxide

oxygen

nitrogen

helium

3.17 Fertilizers and ammonia

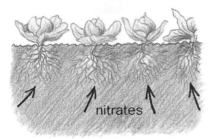

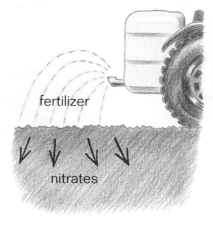

For healthy growth, plants need nitrogen. To get it, they take nitrates from the soil.

If crops are picked, they cannot rot and put nitrates back into the soil, so....

farmers add fertilizers to the soil to replace the nitrates (and other minerals).

▶ Making ammonia

Ammonia is a smelly gas. It is a compound of nitrogen and hydrogen. It is produced in a chemical works. Here is the word equation for the reaction which makes ammonia:

nitrogen + hydrogen → ammonia

Ammonia is used to make nitric acid and chemical fertilizers.

▶ Making nitric acid

In a chemical works, nitric acid is produced by a series of reactions.

Nitric acid is used to make explosives, plastics, and drugs. But it is mainly used to make a fertilizer called **Nitram**.

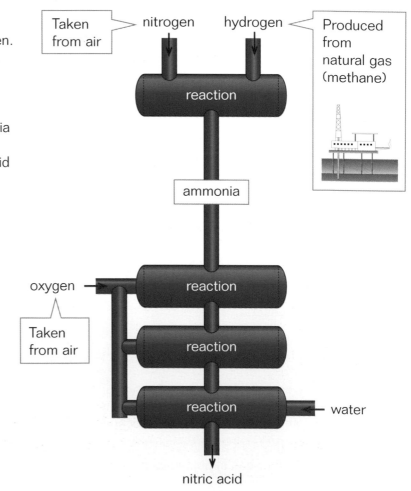

▶ Making Nitram fertilizer

Nitram is another name for ammonium nitrate. Here is the word equation for the reaction which makes it:

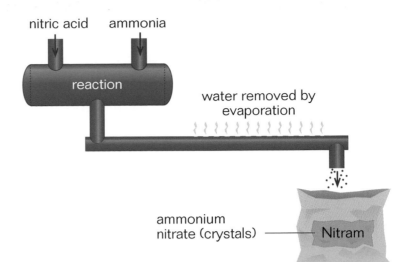

nitric acid   ammonia

reaction

water removed by evaporation

ammonium nitrate (crystals) —— Nitram

$$\underset{\text{acid}}{\text{nitric acid}} + \underset{\text{alkali}}{\text{ammonia}} \rightarrow \underset{\text{salt}}{\text{ammonium nitrate}}$$

The alkali neutralizes the acid to produce the salt. For more examples of reactions with acids producing salts, see spread 3.11.

▶ Problems with fertilizers

This is what can happen if too much fertilizer is put on the soil:

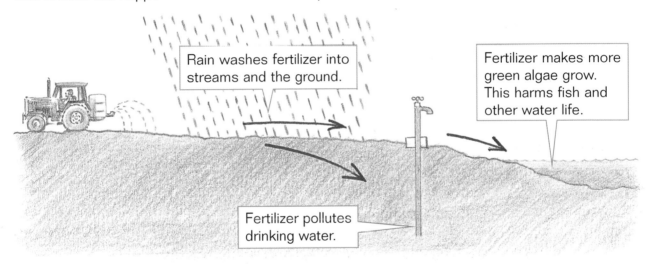

Rain washes fertilizer into streams and the ground.

Fertilizer makes more green algae grow. This harms fish and other water life.

Fertilizer pollutes drinking water.

1 Write down the substance on the right which goes with each of these. (You can choose the same substance more than once.)
   a This is made when nitrogen reacts with hydrogen.
   b This is an alkali.
   c This is a fertilizer called Nitram.
   d This is made when nitric acid reacts with ammonia.
   e This is a salt.

   ammonium nitrate

   nitrogen

   ammonia

2 Copy and complete this sentence:
   If crops are picked, farmers put fertilizer on the soil because....

3 Write down *two* problems caused by putting too much fertilizer on soil.

3.18 Water

Here are some facts about water:

- Two-thirds of the Earth's surface is covered with water.
- All living things need water.
- Our bodies are two-thirds water.
- Water can be a solid (ice), a liquid, or a gas (water vapour).

▶ The water cycle

The Earth's water is recycled - it is used over and over again. This is called the *water cycle*:

| The Sun heats the sea. Water evaporates. | The water vapour rises. It condenses to form clouds. A cloud is millions of tiny droplets of water (or ice). | Clouds release their water as rain (or snow). |

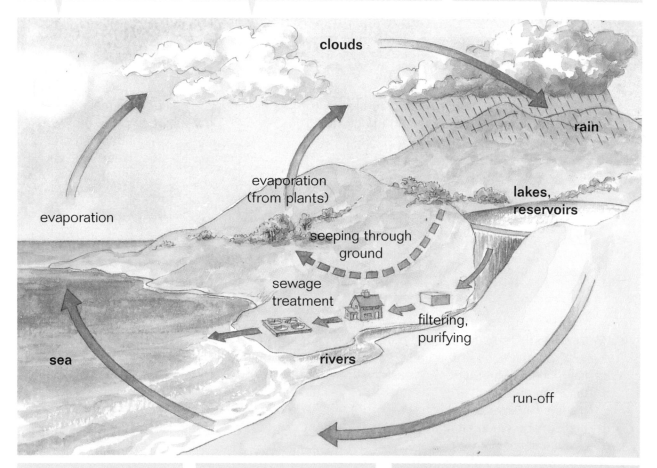

| Rain seeps into the ground, runs into streams and rivers, and flows back into the sea. | Plants take water from the soil. Some goes back into the air as vapour. | Reservoirs trap water for our homes. Waste water and sewage is put back into the sea (it may be purified first). |

▶ Freezing water

Water freezes at 0 °C.

When water freezes it expands. It takes up more space than before.

The force of the expansion can be huge.

This much water…   …becomes this much ice

Here are some of the effects of freezing water:

Water vapour condenses on cold ground or plants to form *dew*. When dew freezes, it is called *frost*.

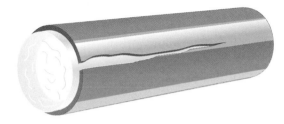

Pipes burst when water in them freezes.

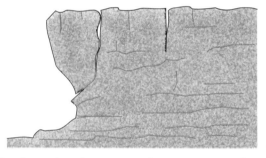

Rocks split when water freezes in cracks.

1 Write out these sentences in the correct order, starting with the one about the Sun:
   The Sun heats the surface of the sea.
   Water flows out to sea.
   Water evaporates from the sea.
   Rainwater runs into lakes and rivers.
   Rain falls to the ground.
   Water vapour condenses to form clouds.

2 Describe *two* ways in which water in the ground can get back into the air.

3 Copy and complete these sentences:
   Dew is formed when....
   Frozen dew is called.....
   When water pipes freeze, they burst because.....

Rock, stone, and soil

▶ Weathering

If rock or stonework is exposed (out in the open), it is weakened by the weather. This is called **weathering**.

The effects of weathering on stonework.

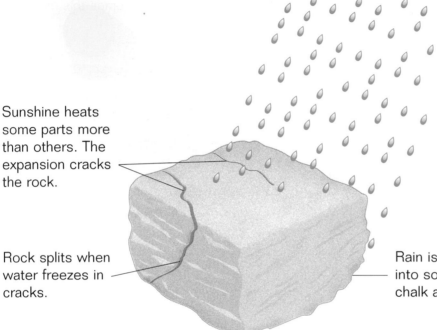

Sunshine heats some parts more than others. The expansion cracks the rock.

Rock splits when water freezes in cracks.

Rain is slightly acid. It eats into some rocks, such as chalk and limestone.

▶ Soil

Soil is mainly made from the rock underneath it. The rock gets broken up by rain, frost, and expansion caused by the Sun's heat.

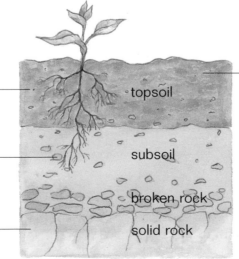

Soil is made from the smaller bits of broken rock.

Stones are the bigger bits of broken rock.

Under the soil, there is solid rock.

topsoil

subsoil

broken rock

solid rock

Topsoil has rotting plant and animal waste in it. This is called **humus**. It is rich in the minerals that plants need.

▶ The rock cycle

Materials from rocks are used over and over again. This is called the *rock cycle*. It can take millions of years. Here is one part of it:

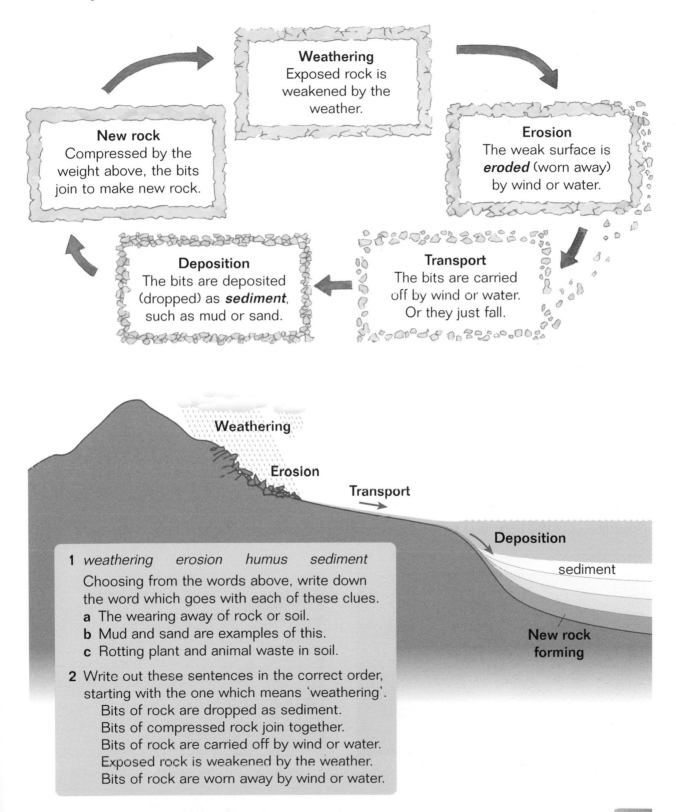

Weathering
Exposed rock is weakened by the weather.

Erosion
The weak surface is *eroded* (worn away) by wind or water.

New rock
Compressed by the weight above, the bits join to make new rock.

Deposition
The bits are deposited (dropped) as *sediment*, such as mud or sand.

Transport
The bits are carried off by wind or water. Or they just fall.

Weathering

Erosion

Transport

Deposition

sediment

New rock forming

1 *weathering   erosion   humus   sediment*
  Choosing from the words above, write down the word which goes with each of these clues.
  a The wearing away of rock or soil.
  b Mud and sand are examples of this.
  c Rotting plant and animal waste in soil.

2 Write out these sentences in the correct order, starting with the one which means 'weathering'.
  Bits of rock are dropped as sediment.
  Bits of compressed rock join together.
  Bits of rock are carried off by wind or water.
  Exposed rock is weakened by the weather.
  Bits of rock are worn away by wind or water.

Looking at rocks

The Earth is made of rock. Deep in the Earth, the rock is so hot that it is *molten* (melted). Sometimes, molten rock comes out of volcanoes, as in the photograph.

The Earth's surface changes slowly over millions of years. Rocks in the ground may be raised up and exposed. Other rocks may be buried.

There are three main types of rocks:

▶ Igneous rocks

These are made of tiny crystals. They are formed when molten rock cools and goes solid.

Examples

Granite This went solid underground. It was exposed when rocks above it were worn away.

Basalt This formed from molten rock which oozed out of cracks in the Earth.

▶ Sedimentary rocks

These are made from layers of sediment dropped by water, wind, or moving ice. The sediment is compressed by the weight above and sets like concrete. But this takes millions of years.

Examples

Sandstone This formed from bits worn away from other rocks.

Limestone This formed from the shells and bones of ancient sea creatures.

▶ Metamorphic rocks

Deep underground, igneous and sedimentary rocks can be changed by heat or pressure. They become *metamorphic* ('changed') rocks.

Examples

Marble This formed from *limestone* when it was heated underground.

Slate This formed from *shale (mudstone)* when it was compressed underground.

▶ Using rocks

We get minerals, such as diamond and gold, from rocks. The word 'mineral' really means anything useful that can be mined from the Earth.

The table shows some more uses of rocks.

Rock	Description	Examples of use
Granite	Very hard, sparkling	chippings, road stone building stone
Limestone	light colour	building/facing stone chippings in cement, concrete
Marble	light colour, hard, smooth	facing stone statues
Slate	hard, but splits into flat sheets	roofing tiles snooker tables

1 *igneous   sedimentary   metamorphic*
   Copy these sentences. Fill in the blanks using the words above.
   a Rocks formed from bits of rock or shell, dropped in layers, are called ____ rocks.
   b Rocks formed when molten rock cools and goes solid are called ____ rocks.
   c Rocks changed by heat or pressure are called ____ rocks.

2 Copy the table on the right. Fill in the blanks by giving one example of each type of rock and one use for that rock. (The name of one rock has been written in for you.)

Rock	Used for
igneous: *granite*	
sedimentary:	
metamorphic:	

Fossils and folds

▶ **Strata....**

When sedimentary rocks are formed, the layers build up one on top of another. On a cliff, you can see these layers because the rock has been cut away.

The layers are called **strata**. They take millions of years to build up.

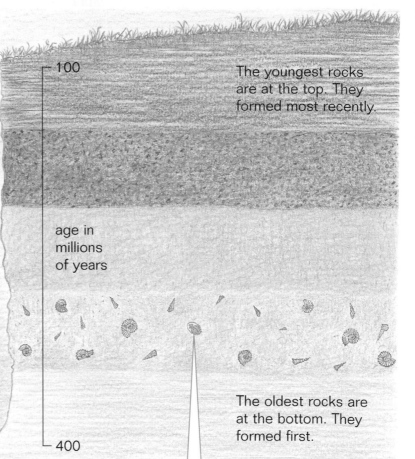

100

The youngest rocks are at the top. They formed most recently.

age in millions of years

400

The oldest rocks are at the bottom. They formed first.

▶ **.....and fossils**

Sedimentary rocks sometimes have **fossils** in. These formed from the remains of plants and animals which lived millions of years ago.

 ▶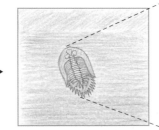

Fossil of a trilobite which died over 300 million years ago.

When this trilobite died, it was trapped in sediment. Its body was slowly replaced by minerals, forming a hard, stony fossil.

There are no fossils in igneous rocks. When the rocks were molten, the heat would have destroyed any plant or animal remains.

▶ Folds in the crust

In some places, layers of rocks have huge *folds* in them.

These folded rocks are at Lulworth Cove in Dorset. ▶

Sometimes rocks can be folded so much that the layers are turned upside-down.

This is how folds are formed:

The Earth has a rocky outer layer called the *crust*. Pieces of crust 'float' like huge rafts on more flexible rocks underneath.

If pieces of crust move towards each other, the rocks between them gets buckled. This produces folds and mountains.

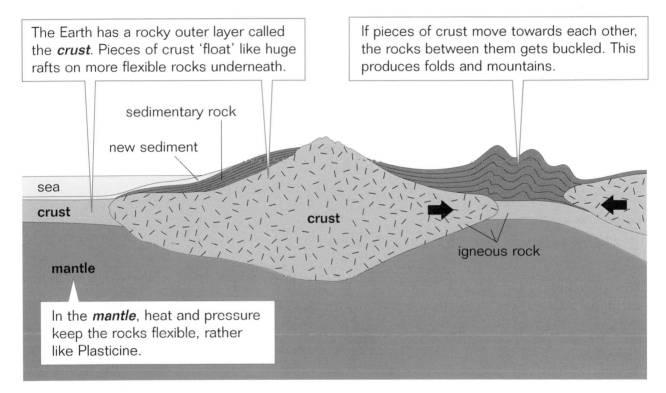

sedimentary rock

new sediment

sea

crust

crust

igneous rock

mantle

In the *mantle*, heat and pressure keep the rocks flexible, rather like Plasticine.

---

1 Write down a word which means:
   a layers of rock.
   b the Earth's outer layer.

2 Look at the diagram on the right. Then copy and complete this sentence (you need to write A or B in the first space):
   Fossil .... is likely to be the oldest because.....

3 Copy and complete these sentences:
   Layers of rocks get folded because.....
   There are no fossils in igneous rocks because.....

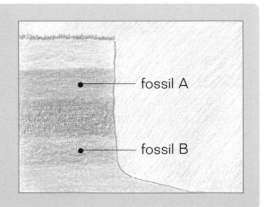

fossil A

fossil B

Moving continents

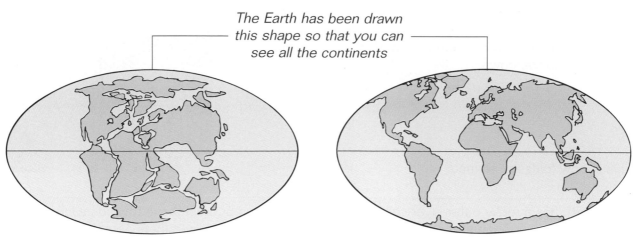

The Earth has been drawn this shape so that you can see all the continents

200 million years ago　　　　　　　Today

The Earth's continents are huge pieces of crust which 'float' on the mantle underneath. Scientists think that, millions of years ago, there was one giant continent. This split into pieces which slowly moved apart. The pieces are still moving - by just a few centimetres a year.

▶ Inside the Earth

This is what scientists think the Earth is like inside:

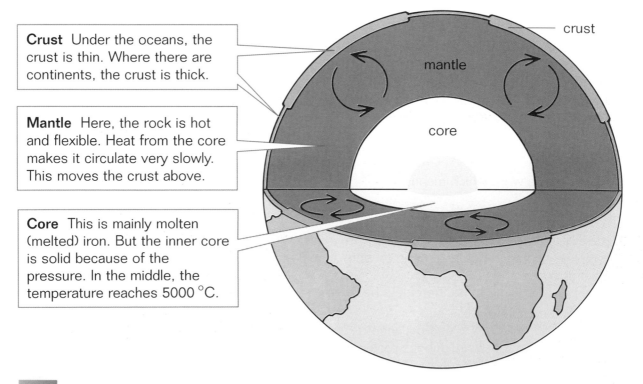

Crust Under the oceans, the crust is thin. Where there are continents, the crust is thick.

Mantle Here, the rock is hot and flexible. Heat from the core makes it circulate very slowly. This moves the crust above.

Core This is mainly molten (melted) iron. But the inner core is solid because of the pressure. In the middle, the temperature reaches 5000 °C.

crust

mantle

core

▶ Plates and earthquakes

The large pieces of moving crust (and upper mantle) are called **plates**. Where plates slide or push against each other, there may be earthquakes.

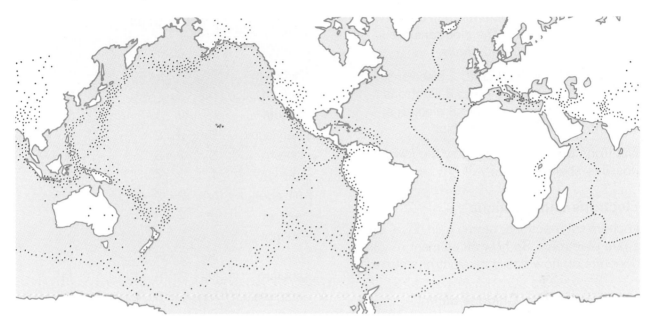

Each red dot on this map shows where an earthquake has happened in the last 20 years. Together, the red dots show where the different plates meet.

▶ Volcanoes

Most volcanoes are near plate edges, where the crust is cracked and weak. Hot rock in the mantle turns liquid and is pushed out from volcanoes as **lava**.

1 *crust   mantle   plate*
  core   lava

Choose the word above which goes with each of these:
  a Molten rock from a volcano.
  b This is thickest where there are continents.
  c The very hot centre of the Earth.
  d Large piece of crust (and upper mantle).

2 Copy and complete these sentences:
  a Earthquakes usually happen near plate edges because....
  b The continents seem to fit together like a jigsaw because....

119

3.23 Atoms and bonds

▶ Elements and electron shells

Each element has a different number of electrons in its atom. The electrons are arranged in layers called **shells**:

The 1st shell can hold up to 2 electrons.
The 2nd shell can hold up to 8 electrons.
The 3rd shell can hold up to 8 electrons.
There are more shells after this.

Electrons always try to occupy the *lowest* possible shell.

▶ Electrons and reactions

In chemical reactions, atoms gain, lose, or share electrons. So how an element reacts depends on how easily its electrons move.

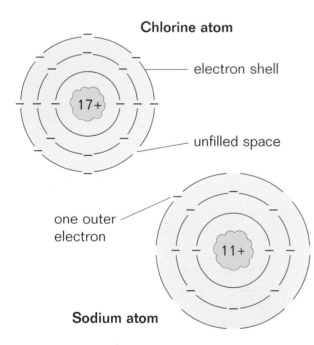

Chlorine atom

— electron shell

— unfilled space

one outer electron

Sodium atom

Chlorine has one unfilled space in its outer shell. It easily gains an electron from another atom, so it is very reactive.

Sodium has one outer electron which it easily loses. So it is very reactive.

Helium has a full outer shell. Its electrons tend to stay where they are, so it is very unreactive.

Element and symbols		Number of electrons				
		Shell				
		1	2	3	4	Total
hydrogen	H	1				1
helium	He	2				2
lithium	Li	2	1			3
beryllium	Be	2	2			4
boron	B	2	3			5
carbon	C	2	4			6
nitrogen	N	2	5			7
oxygen	O	2	6			8
fluorine	F	2	7			9
neon	Ne	2	8			10
sodium	Na	2	8	1		11
magnesium	Mg	2	8	2		12

full shell (helium, total 2)

full shell (neon, total 10)

This is also the **proton number**. An atom has the same number of electrons as protons.

▶ Isotopes

Here are two versions of a carbon atom - one has more neutrons. Different versions of the same element are called **isotopes**:

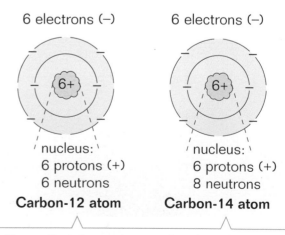

6 electrons (–)   6 electrons (–)

nucleus: nucleus:
6 protons (+)   6 protons (+)
6 neutrons   8 neutrons

Carbon-12 atom   **Carbon-14 atom**

This called the **mass number**. It is the number of protons plus neutrons.

Over 98% of carbon atoms are of carbon-12.

▶ Ions

If an atom gains or loses one or more electrons, it becomes an *ion*.

When a chlorine atom gains an electron (−), it becomes a negative (−) ion.

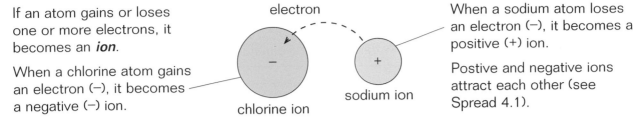

electron

chlorine ion

sodium ion

When a sodium atom loses an electron (−), it becomes a positive (+) ion.

Postive and negative ions attract each other (see Spread 4.1).

▶ Bonds

Atoms are held to each other by forces called *bonds*.

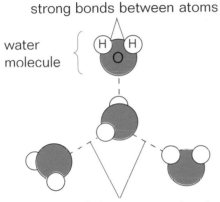

strong bonds between atoms

water molecule

weak bonds between molecules

In a molecule, the atoms share some of their electrons. The shared electrons bond the atoms together strongly.

In molecular solids, like ice, the bonds *between* molecules are weak. So these solids have *low* melting points (temperatures).

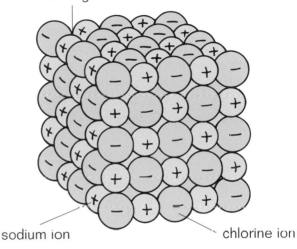

strong bond between ions

sodium ion

chlorine ion

In sodium choride (common salt), the bonds are the attractions between negative and positive ions.

In ionic solids, like salt, the bonds are strong and difficult to break. So these solids have *high* melting points.

---

1 How many electrons can an atom have in its **a** 1st shell **b** 2nd shell **c** 3rd shell?

2 **a** Copy and complete the table below to show how the electrons are arranged.
   b Which of the two elements would you expect to be least reactive? Why?

Element	Number of electrons				
	Shell				Total
	1	2	3	4	
argon					18
potassium					19

3 What is the difference between a sodium atom and a sodium ion?

4 **a** What is the proton number of lithium?
   b Copy and complete the table below to show the numbers of particles in the isotopes lithium–6 and lithium–7.

	Number of......		
	electrons	protons	neutrons
lithium-6			
lithium-7			

3.24 The periodic table

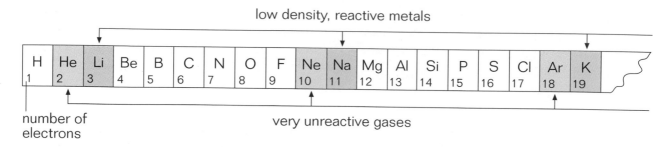

low density, reactive metals

| H 1 | He 2 | Li 3 | Be 4 | B 5 | C 6 | N 7 | O 8 | F 9 | Ne 10 | Na 11 | Mg 12 | Al 13 | Si 14 | P 15 | S 16 | Cl 17 | Ar 18 | K 19 |

number of electrons

very unreactive gases

The elements above have been arranged in order of number of electrons. Along the row, some properties follow a periodic (repeating) pattern. Using observations like this, scientists have made a chart of the elements. It is called the *periodic table*.

In the periodic table (below), the elements are arranged in rows, called *periods*, one on top of another. Some of the columns have *group* numbers. Elements in the same group have similar properties because their outer electron shells are similar.

Periodic table

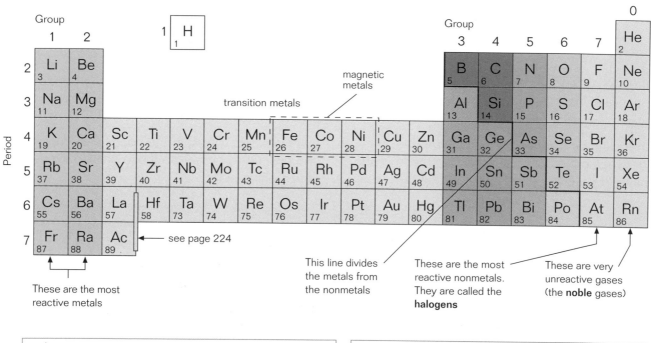

These are the most reactive metals

This line divides the metals from the nonmetals

These are the most reactive nonmetals. They are called the **halogens**

These are very unreactive gases (the **noble** gases)

magnetic metals

transition metals

see page 224

Transition metals

These include....

| Fe iron | Ni nickel | Cu copper |

- They have high melting points.
- They form coloured compounds.
- They are often good *catalysts* (see 3.26).
- For other properties, see **Metals** in 3.3.

Group 0: noble gases

These are unreactive because they have full outer shells. They are also colourless. (For uses of helium, neon, and argon, see 3.16.)

He helium
Ne neon
Ar argon

Group 1: alkali metals

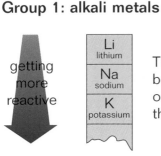

getting more reactive

These are reactive because they have one electron in their outer shell.

Sodium is a soft, low-density metal. It reacts violently with water to form sodium hydroxide and hydrogen:

sodium + water → sodium hydroxide + hydrogen

Sodium hydroxide is a strong alkali, which is why sodium is called an alkali metal.

Sodium

Potassium is also a soft, low density metal which reacts violently with water.

Group 7: halogens

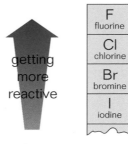

getting more reactive

These are reactive because they have one unfilled space in their outer shell.

Chlorine is a poisonous green gas. It bleaches damp litmus paper (removes its colour), so this can be used as a test for chlorine.

For uses of chlorine, see Spread 3.25.

Bromine is a harmful red liquid which gives off a brown vapour.

Bromine vapour

Iodine is a dark solid which gives off a purple vapour.

To answer these questions, you may need to look at the full periodic table on page 224 (the last page of the book).

1 *potassium   fluorine   cobalt   lithium   aluminium   krypton   bromine   oxygen*

   Choose the element above which matches each of the following:

   a A halogen which is more reactive than chlorine.
   b An alkali metal which is more reactive than sodium.
   c A transition metal.
   d A noble gas.
   e Its atoms each have 8 electrons.

2 Name *three* elements which have one electron in their outer shell.

3 Name *three* elements which have one unfilled space in their outer shell.

4 Name *three* elements which have a full outer shell.

5 Write down *two* properties which the elements in Group 1 have in common.

6 Write down *two* properties which the elements in Group 0 have in common.

3.25 Further reactions

▶ Acids and bases...

A base is a substance that can neutralize an acid by forming a salt and water:

acid + base → salt + water

For example:

hydrochloric acid + sodium hydroxide → sodium chloride + water

A base that dissolves in water is called an *alkali*. Sodium hydroxide dissolves in water, so it is an alkali (see Spread 3.7).

The above reaction is an example of a *neutralization* reaction.

pH scale

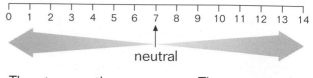

neutral

The stronger the acid, the lower the number

The stronger the alkali, the higher the number

The *pH scale* is used to measure how strong or weak an acid or alkali is.

You can measure pH using *universal indicator*. This goes a different colour, depending on the pH of the solution.

▶ Oxides

Nonmetals react with oxygen to form oxides such as....

carbon dioxide   sulphur dioxide
nitrogen dioxide   phosphorus pentoxide

These form acidic solutions when dissolved in water, so they are called *acidic oxides*.

Metals react with oxygen to form oxides such as....

sodium oxide   magnesium oxide
calcium oxide   copper(II) oxide

These can neutralize acids, so they are called *basic oxides*.

▶ Reactivity

Some metals react more readily than others. Scientists have worked out a *reactivity series* for metals.

Most metals are found in compounds. The higher up the series, the more difficult it is to separate a metal from its compounds.

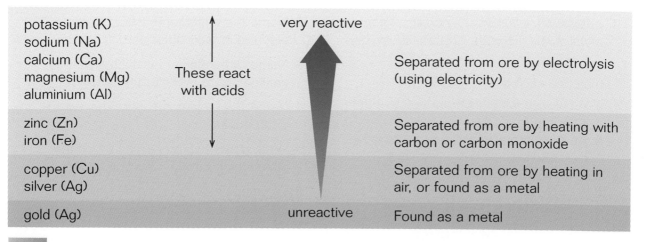

potassium (K)
sodium (Na)
calcium (Ca)   very reactive
magnesium (Mg)
aluminium (Al)   These react   Separated from ore by electrolysis
                      with acids   (using electricity)

zinc (Zn)
iron (Fe)   Separated from ore by heating with
                                         carbon or carbon monoxide

copper (Cu)   Separated from ore by heating in
silver (Ag)   air, or found as a metal

gold (Ag)   unreactive   Found as a metal

Electrolysis

If a compound is liquid and contains ions, it can be separated into simpler substances using electricity. This is called *electrolysis*.

On the right, aluminium is being produced from its ore (aluminium oxide) by electrolysis. The liquid is called the *electrolyte*. In it, aluminium oxide splits into aluminium ions (+) and oxide ions (−). The aluminium ions are attracted to the *cathode* (−), where they become aluminium atoms. These collect at the bottom of the tank as pure, molten aluminium.

Made from salt

On Earth, there is lots of sodium chloride (common salt) in the sea and underground. Electrolysis is used to get useful substances from sodium choride solution.

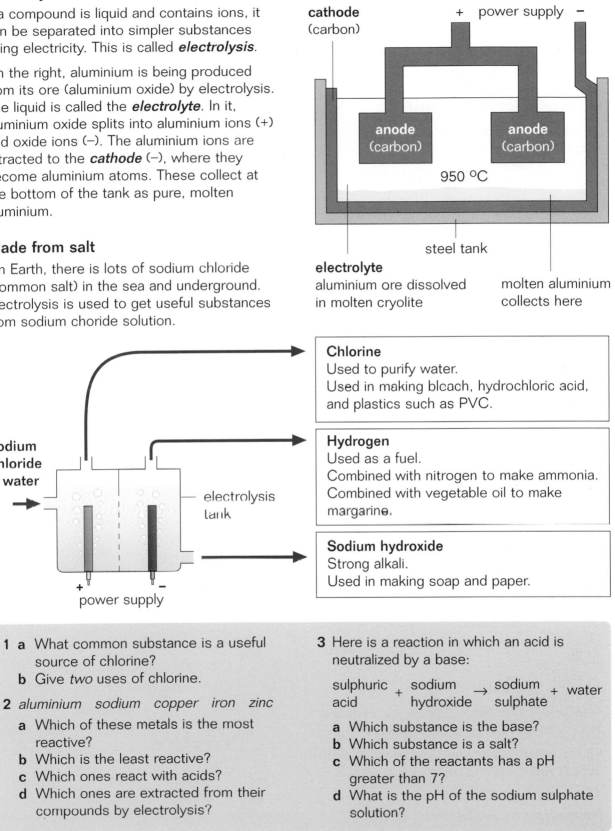

cathode
(carbon)

+ power supply −

anode
(carbon)

anode
(carbon)

950 °C

steel tank

electrolyte
aluminium ore dissolved
in molten cryolite

molten aluminium
collects here

sodium
chloride
+ water

electrolysis
tank

+   −
power supply

Chlorine
Used to purify water.
Used in making bleach, hydrochloric acid, and plastics such as PVC.

Hydrogen
Used as a fuel.
Combined with nitrogen to make ammonia.
Combined with vegetable oil to make margarine.

Sodium hydroxide
Strong alkali.
Used in making soap and paper.

1 a What common substance is a useful source of chlorine?
  b Give *two* uses of chlorine.

2 *aluminium   sodium   copper   iron   zinc*
  a Which of these metals is the most reactive?
  b Which is the least reactive?
  c Which ones react with acids?
  d Which ones are extracted from their compounds by electrolysis?

3 Here is a reaction in which an acid is neutralized by a base:

sulphuric + sodium → sodium + water
acid   hydroxide   sulphate

  a Which substance is the base?
  b Which substance is a salt?
  c Which of the reactants has a pH greater than 7?
  d What is the pH of the sodium sulphate solution?

3.26 Equations and reactions

▶ Equations and formulae

On the right, you can see how the atoms regroup when hydrogen and oxygen react to form water.

The equation for the reaction has been written using chemical symbols. In the equation, each substance has its own *formula*: for example, H_2O for water.

Letters in brackets tell you whether a substance is solid *(s)*, liquid *(l)*, gas *(g)*, or a solution in water *(aq)* *(aq = aqueous)*.

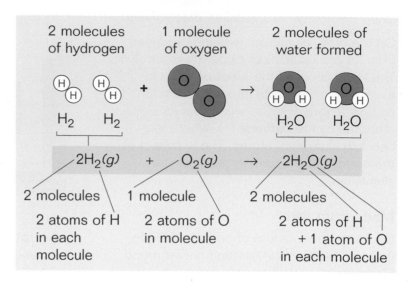

2 molecules of hydrogen   1 molecule of oxygen   2 molecules of water formed

H_2 H_2 +   O   → H_2O H_2O

$$2H_2(g) \quad + \quad O_2(g) \quad \rightarrow \quad 2H_2O(g)$$

2 molecules   1 molecule   2 molecules

2 atoms of H in each molecule   2 atoms of O in molecule   2 atoms of H + 1 atom of O in each molecule

▶ Types of chemical reaction

Combination Two substances join to make a one new compound. For example:

magnesium + oxygen → magnesium oxide

Thermal decomposition When heated, a compound splits into simpler substances. For example:

calcium carbonate (limestone) $\xrightarrow{\text{heat}}$ calcium oxide (quicklime) + carbon dioxide (gas)

Redox When hydrogen gas is passed over hot copper(II) oxide, this reaction takes place:

copper(II) oxide + hydrogen → copper + water

$$CuO(s) + H_2(g) \rightarrow Cu(s) + H_2O(g)$$

Copper(II) oxide *loses* oxygen: it is **reduced**. Hydrogen *gains* oxygen: it is **oxidized**.

This is called a **redox** reaction because there is both **red**uction and **ox**idation.

Neutralization See Spread 3.25

Exothermic and endothermic If a reaction releases energy as heat, it is **exothermic**: If it takes in energy, it is **endothermic**.

Precipitation Two solutions mix, react, and give a product which is insoluble (it doesn't dissolve). It appears as tiny, solid bits called a **precipitate**. For example:

sodium chloride solution

silver nitrate solution

precipitate: silver chloride

silver nitrate (soluble) + sodium chloride (soluble) → silver chloride (insoluble) + sodium nitrate (soluble)

Displacement One substance displaces (pushes out and replaces) a less reactive one:

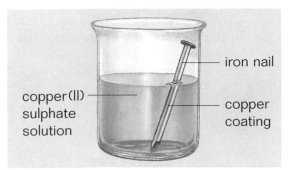

- iron nail
- copper(II) sulphate solution
- copper coating

Iron dissolves and displaces copper from the solution. The copper is deposited on the nail:

$$\text{iron} + \frac{\text{copper(II)}}{\text{sulphate}} \rightarrow \text{copper} + \frac{\text{iron(II)}}{\text{sulphate}}$$

When a metal reacts with an acid, hydrogen is displaced from the solution (see Spread 3.11).

Reversible Depending on conditions, some reactions can work in either direction. For example:

$$\text{nitrogen} + \text{hydrogen} \rightleftharpoons \text{ammonia}$$

The symbol $\rightleftharpoons$ means that ammonia can also break down into nitrogen and hydrogen.

▶ Rate of reaction

The rate (speed) of a reaction depends on how quickly the reacting atoms, ions, or molecules meet. These factors have an effect:

Size of bits Powdered substances react more quickly than larger lumps.

Temperature If this rises, a reaction goes faster.

Concentration If the reactants are more concentrated, the reaction is faster.

Adding a catalyst See below.

▶ Catalysts and enzymes

A *catalyst* is a substance which speeds up a reaction without being used up itself. For example, iron is a catalyst for this reaction:

$$\text{nitrogen} + \text{hydrogen} \xrightarrow{\text{iron}} \text{ammonia}$$

An *enzyme* is a biological catalyst. It works best at one particular temperature. Ethanol (alcohol) is made from the glucose in grapes or grain using enzymes in yeast:

$$\text{glucose} \xrightarrow{\text{enzymes}} \text{ethanol} + \text{carbon dioxide}$$

This process is called *fermentation*. It is used to make beer and wine.

---

1 When iron is placed in copper(II) sulphate solution, this reaction takes place:

$$\text{iron} + \frac{\text{copper(II)}}{\text{sulphate}} \rightarrow \text{copper} + \frac{\text{iron(II)}}{\text{sulphate}}$$

  a What element is displaced from the solution? What element replaces it?
  b Which one is the more reactive?

2 When sulphur dioxide, SO_2, reacts with oxygen, O_2, sulphur trioxide is formed:

$$2SO_2(g) + O_2(g) \rightleftharpoons 2SO_3(g)$$

  a What does the symbol (g) stand for?
  b What does the symbol $\rightleftharpoons$ tell you?
  c How many atoms of oxygen are there in one molecule of sulphur trioxide?

3 Give *three* ways of changing the rate of a chemical reaction.

4 When the things below are made, what job is done by the enzymes in yeast?

3.27 Atmosphere and rocks

▶ Changes in the Earth's atmosphere

4500 million years ago, the Earth was a hot, new planet (see 4.33).

As the Earth cooled, and life developed, its atmosphere slowly changed.

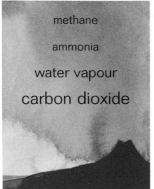

methane

ammonia

water vapour

carbon dioxide

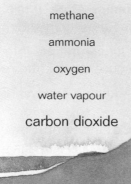

methane

ammonia

oxygen

water vapour

carbon dioxide

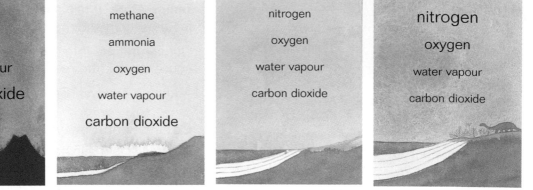

nitrogen

oxygen

water vapour

carbon dioxide

nitrogen

oxygen

water vapour

carbon dioxide

4000 million years ago, the atmosphere was mainly gases from volcanoes. As the Earth cooled, water vapour condensed to form oceans.

500 million years ago, early plants were giving out oxygen, some of which reacted with the methane and ammonia. In time, most of the carbon (from carbon dioxide) became locked up in sedimentary rocks, and microbes were producing nitrogen.

200 million years ago, the atmosphere was similar to that of today. It is now mainly nitrogen (78%) and oxygen (21%).

▶ Forming igneous rocks

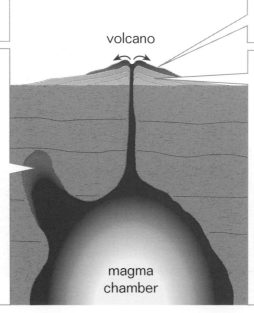

Hot, molten rock in the Earth is called *magma*.

Sometimes, magma comes out of volcanoes, as *lava*.

volcano

Intrusive igneous rock is formed when magma cools and solidifies underground.

Extrusive igneous rock is formed when lava cools and solidifies above the ground.

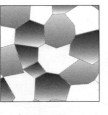

Granite

Basalt

In the ground, magma cools *slowly*, so *large* crystals have time to form.

magma chamber

Above the ground, lava cools *quickly* and forms *small* crystals.

▶ Recycling rocks

Some rocks are lifted up by the slow movements in the Earth's crust. Others may be carried down into the mantle.

Over millions of years, new rocks are formed from the materials in old ones. The diagram below shows the many different parts of the *rock cycle*:

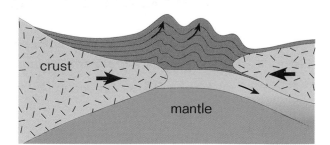

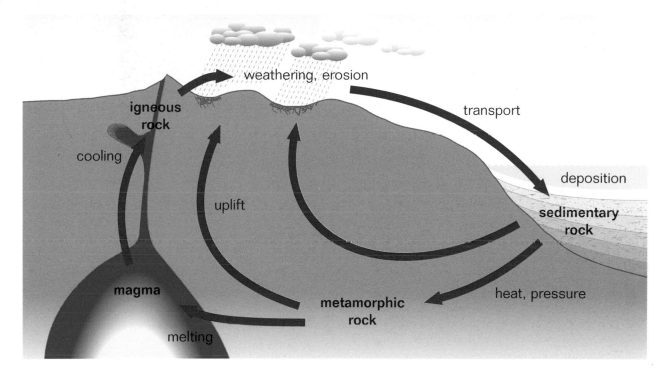

1 Compared with the early atmosphere, why does our atmosphere now have
   a less water vapour?
   b more oxygen?

2 Look at the diagram on the right. Then choose a letter (J-N) which marks each of the following regions:
   a The oldest layer of lava.
   b The youngest layer of lava.
   c A region of sedimentary rock.
   d A region of magma.
   e A region where intrusive igneous rock will form.

3 Look at the diagram on the right. Then explain why metamorphic rock is likely to form at X.

4 Explain why lava coming from a volcano might be made material which was once in sedimentary rock on the ground.

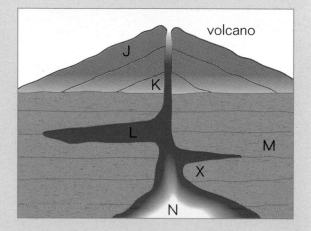

4.1 Charges in action

'Electricity' is another word for **electric charge**.
The photograph shows electric charge in action.

▶ Charges from the atom

There are two types of electric charge. They are
called **positive (+)** and **negative (-)**. They come
from atoms.

An atom has equal amounts of negative (-) and
positive (+) charge. So the charges balance.

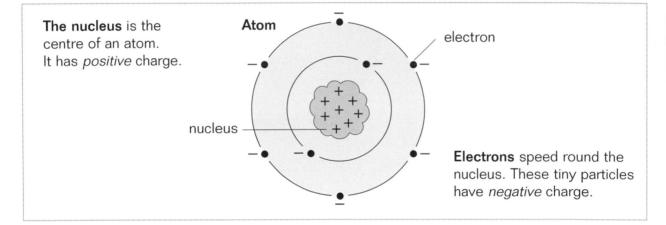

The nucleus is the
centre of an atom.
It has *positive* charge.

Atom

electron

nucleus

Electrons speed round the
nucleus. These tiny particles
have *negative* charge.

▶ From conductors to insulators

Electrons do not always stay with atoms. When you switch on
a light, electrons flow through the wires. A flow of electrons is
called a **current**.

Conductors let electrons flow through.

Insulators do not let electrons flow through.

Conductors	
Good	*Poor*
metals,	human body
especially	water
silver	air
copper	
aluminium	
carbon	

Insulators	
plastics	glass
for example	rubber
PVC	
polythene	
Perspex	

▶ Static electricity

You can charge up an insulator by rubbing it. People say that it has 'static electricity' on it.

If you rub a polythene rod with a cloth, the polythene pulls electrons from the cloth.

The polythene gains negative (−) charge.

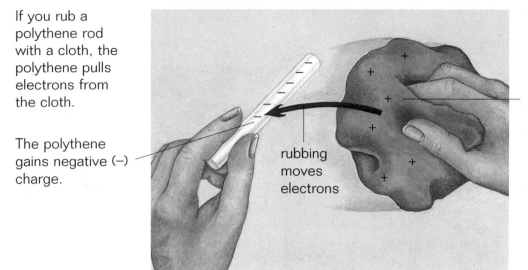

rubbing moves electrons

The cloth is left with positive (+) charge.

Rubbing doesn't make electric charge. It separates charges that are already there.

▶ Forces between charges

When charges are close, they push or pull on each other:

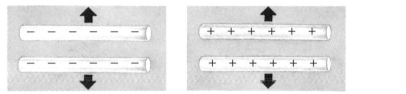

Like charges repel.

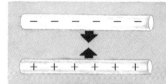

Unlike charges attract.

1 positive   negative

Copy these sentences. Fill in each blank with one of the words above. (You can use the same word more than once.)

The nucleus of an atom has a ___ charge.
An electron has a ___ charge.
A positive charge will attract a ___ charge.
A positive charge will repel a ___ charge.
A negative charge will repel a ___ charge.

2 Copy the table on the right. For each material, put in a tick to show whether it is a *good conductor* of electricity, a *poor conductor*, or an *insulator*. One tick has been done for you.

Material	Good conductor	Poor conductor	Insulator
air		✓	
copper			
glass			
plastic			
aluminium			
carbon			
water			

4.2 A simple circuit

This is called a *circuit*. The *battery* has two *terminals*. It pushes electrons out of the negative (-) terminal, round the circuit, to the positive (+) terminal.

When electrons pass through the bulb, they heat up a *filament* (thin wire) so that it glows.

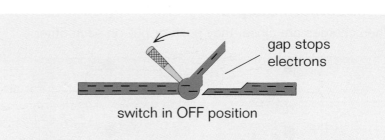

There must be a *complete* circuit for electrons to flow. If there is a break in the circuit, the flow stops, and the bulb goes out. Turning the switch OFF breaks the circuit.

gap stops electrons

switch in OFF position

▶ **Spending energy**

The battery *gives* electrons energy. The electrons *spend* this energy when they flow through the bulb. The bulb sends out energy as heat and light.

For more on energy, see Spread 4.9.

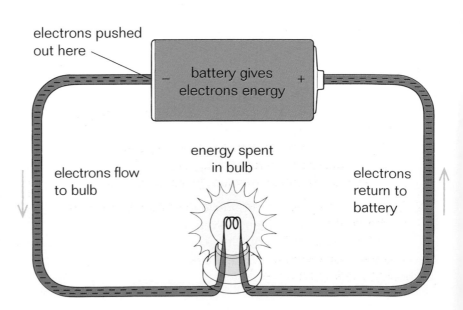

electrons pushed out here

battery gives electrons energy

energy spent in bulb

electrons flow to bulb

electrons return to battery

▶ Voltage

A battery has a **voltage** marked on the side. It is measured in **volts** (**V**). A higher voltage means that each electron has more energy to spend.

To measure the voltage of a battery, you connect a **voltmeter** across its terminals.

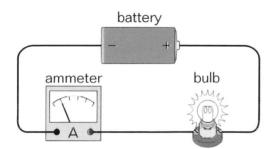

voltmeter

one battery

1.5 volt battery

▶ Current

Current is measured in **amperes** (**A**). A higher current means a bigger flow of electrons.

To measure current, you connect an **ammeter** into the circuit.

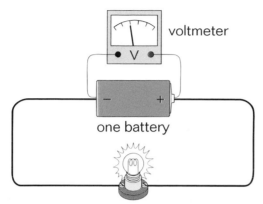

battery

ammeter   bulb

The ammeter can be put anywhere in this circuit, because the current is the same all the way round.

Putting in the ammeter doesn't affect the current.

---

1 *current   voltage   ammeter   voltmeter*

Copy these sentences. Fill in the blanks, choosing words from those above. (You can use the same word more than once.)

Current is measured with a meter called an ____.
____ is measured in amperes.
If there is a break in a circuit, there is no ____.

2 Copy and complete these statements about the circuit on the right:

Meter Y is called a ......
Meter X is called a ......
The reading on meter X is ......

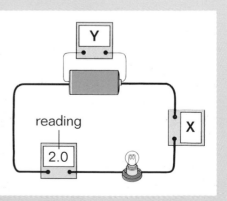

reading

2.0

Y

X

Batteries and bulbs

▶ Adding batteries

This circuit has one battery in it. The voltmeter is measuring the voltage across the battery.

A single battery is sometimes called a *cell*.

voltmeter

one battery

If *two* batteries are put in the circuit like this, the total voltage is twice what it was before. Also, the bulb glows more brightly because a higher current is being pushed through it.

When batteries are connected in a line like this, they are in *series*.

voltmeter reading doubled

two batteries in series

bulb brighter

▶ Circuit symbols

Scientists and electricians draw circuits using *symbols*.

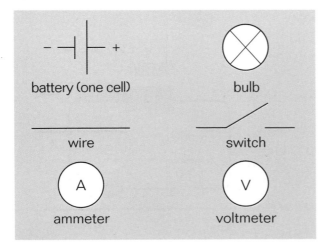

battery (one cell)

bulb

wire

switch

A
ammeter

V
voltmeter

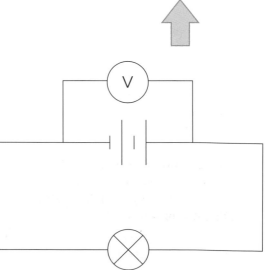

The second circuit, drawn using symbols.

Bulbs in series

This circuit has two bulbs in it. The bulbs are connected in *series* (in a line):

The bulbs glow dimly. It is more difficult for the electrons to pass through two bulbs than one, so there is less current than before.

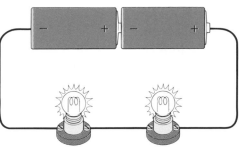

bulbs in series

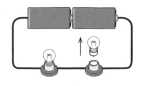

If one bulb is removed, the circuit is broken. So the other bulb goes off.

Bulbs in parallel

This circuit also has two bulbs in it. The bulbs are connected in *parallel*.

The bulbs glow brightly because each is getting the full battery voltage.

Together, two bright bulbs take more current than a single bright bulb, so the battery will not last as long.

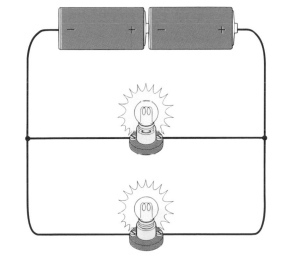

bulbs in parallel

If one bulb is removed, there is still a complete circuit through the other bulb, so it stays bright.

---

1 Look at the circuit A and B on the right.
  a Write down which circuit, A or B, has the brighter bulb.
  b Explain why this bulb is the brighter.

2 Look at the circuits C and D on the right.
  a Write down which circuit, C or D, has two bulbs in series.
  b Write down which circuit, C or D, has the brighter bulbs.
  c Write down what will happen to bulb 1 if bulb 2 is removed.
  d Write down what will happen to bulb 3 if bulb 4 is removed.

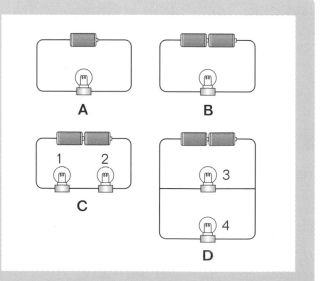

4.4 Resistance, heat, and power

▶ Resistance

Some wires are not such good conductors as others. They have more *resistance* to a flow of electricity.

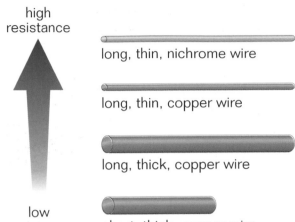

high resistance

long, thin, nichrome wire

long, thin, copper wire

long, thick, copper wire

low resistance

short, thick, copper wire

The resistance of a wire depends on how big it is and what metal it is made of.

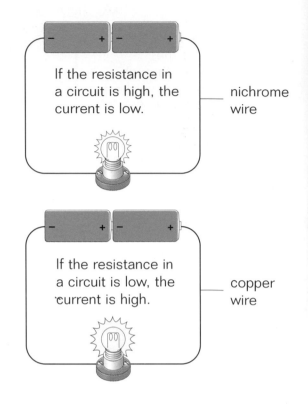

If the resistance in a circuit is high, the current is low.

nichrome wire

If the resistance in a circuit is low, the current is high.

copper wire

Resistors are specially designed to have resistance. They are used in electronic circuits so that each part gets the right amount of current to work properly.

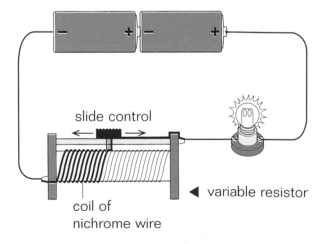

slide control

coil of nichrome wire

◀ variable resistor

Variable resistors have a control so that you can vary the amount of resistance. Using the variable resistor above, you can make the bulb glow brightly or dimly.

Symbol for resistor

Symbol for variable resistor

Heat from resistance

filament
(tungsten wire)

heating elements
(nichrome wire)

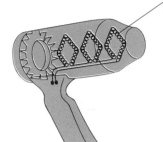

When a current flows through a resistance, heat is given off. This idea is used in a light bulb, where the filament glows white hot. It is also used in the **heating elements** of kettles, irons, toasters, and hairdriers.

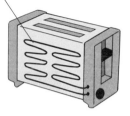

Power

The things above get their energy from the **mains**. Their **power** is marked on them in **watts (W)** or in **kilowatts (kW)**. The higher the power, the quicker they take energy from the mains:

1000 watts
(1 kilowatt)

This iron takes energy ten times as quickly as this lamp

100 watts

1 *power   kilowatt   heat   resistance*
Choose the word above that goes with each of these:
  a Better conductors have less of this.
  b This is given off when a current flows through a resistance.
  c This is measured in watts.
  d This means 1000 watts.

2 Look at circuits A and B on the right. Then copy and complete this sentence:
  The bulb in circuit .... is brightest because....

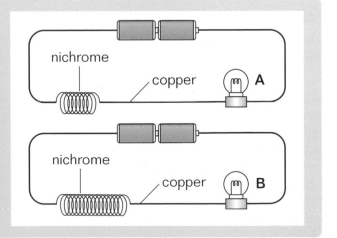

nichrome

copper

A

nichrome

copper

B

Magnets and electromagnets

▶ Magnets

A few metals are *magnetic*. They are attracted to magnets and can be magnetized. Iron and steel are the main magnetic metals.

The force from a magnet seems to come from two points near the ends. These are the *north pole* (*N*) and the *south pole* (*S*) of the magnet.

When the poles of a magnet are brought close, you can feel the force between them:

Magnetic	Non-magnetic
iron	aluminium
steel*	copper
nickel	brass
	tin
* apart from	silver
stainless steel	gold

magnet (steel)

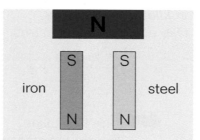

Like poles repel

Unlike poles attract

▶ Magnetizing iron and steel

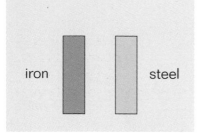

These pieces of iron and steel are unmagnetized.

When a magnet is near, they become magnetized.

The magnet is taken away. Iron loses its magnetism. Steel keeps its magnetism.

▶ Magnetic fields

The space around a magnet is called a *magnetic field*. The field pulls on anything magnetic.

You can use a *compass* to see which way the field is pulling. A compass is a tiny magnet which can turn on a spindle.

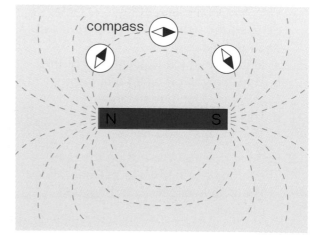

Electromagnet

An electric current produces a magnetic field. This idea is used in an *electromagnet*.

The current in the coil produces a field. The field magnetizes the iron *core*. This makes the field much stronger.

When the electromagnet is switched off, the iron core loses its magnetism and the field vanishes.

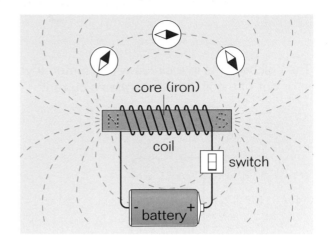

core (iron)

coil

switch

battery

Relay

A *relay* is a switch worked by an electromagnet. With a relay, you can use a tiny switch to turn on a big electric motor powered by mains electricity. The relay works like this:

When you switch on the current in the input circuit, the electromagnet pulls on an iron lever.

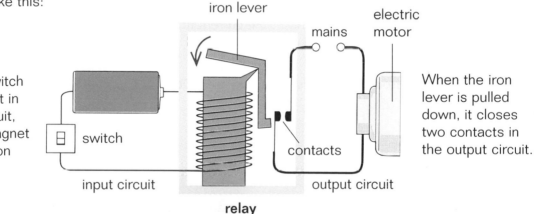

iron lever

mains

electric motor

switch

contacts

input circuit

output circuit

When the iron lever is pulled down, it closes two contacts in the output circuit.

relay

1 *north   south*

   Copy these sentences about magnets. Fill in each blank with one of the words above. (You can use the same word more than once.)
      A north pole will attract a _____ pole.
      A north pole will repel a _____ pole.
      A south pole will repel a _____ pole.

2 Copy the table on the right. For each metal, put in a tick to show whether it is *magnetic* or *non-magnetic*. The first one has been done for you.

3 Write down the name of a metal which:
   a keeps its magnetism when magnetized.
   b loses its magnetism easily.
   c can be used as the core of an electromagnet.

Metal	Magnetic	Non-magnetic
nickel	✓	
iron		
aluminium		
copper		
steel		

Generating electricity

The coil below is in a circuit with a meter. If you move a magnet in or out of a coil, this *generates* a current:

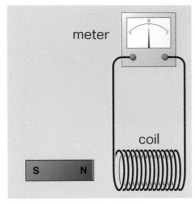

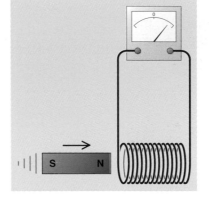

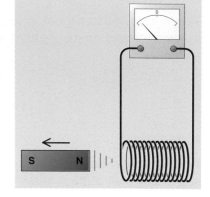

When the magnet is not moving, the meter reads zero.

As the magnet is pushed in, a current flows one way.

As the magnet is pulled out, a current flows the other way.

If you move the magnet in, out, in, out... , the current flows forwards, backwards, forwards, backwards.... . It is an *alternating current (AC)*.

The one-way current from a battery is *direct current (DC)*.

▶ **AC generator**

You can generate AC by rotating a coil in a magnetic field. This is what happens in the *generator* on the right.

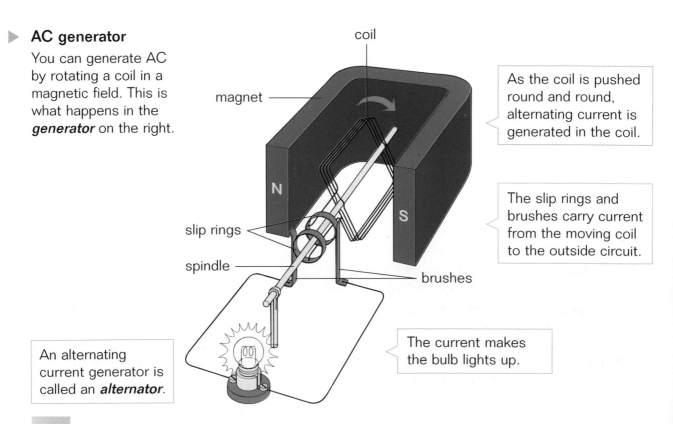

As the coil is pushed round and round, alternating current is generated in the coil.

The slip rings and brushes carry current from the moving coil to the outside circuit.

The current makes the bulb lights up.

An alternating current generator is called an *alternator*.

Electricity for the mains

Mains electricity is AC. It comes from huge generators in **power stations** (see Spread 4.17.)

In a power station, generators like this produce AC at a voltage of 33 000 volts.

More transformers reduce the voltage to 230 volts for the power points in your home.

A **transformer** raises the voltage to 400 000 volts.

The power is sent across country through overhead lines. By using a high voltage, less power is wasted in the lines.

---

1 Look at the diagram on the right.
   Describe what happens
   a as the magnet is pushed into the coil.
   b as the magnet is pulled out of the coil.

2 *transformer   alternator*
   slip ring   alternating current

   Choose the word or words above which goes with each of these:
   a Mains current is this.
   b Another name for an AC generator.
   c Used to change the voltage of AC.

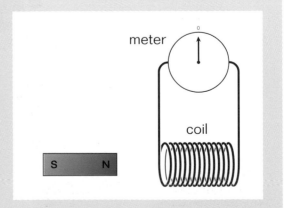

meter

coil

S   N

Electricity from the mains

▶ **Plugging into the mains**

When you plug in a kettle, you are connecting it into a circuit:

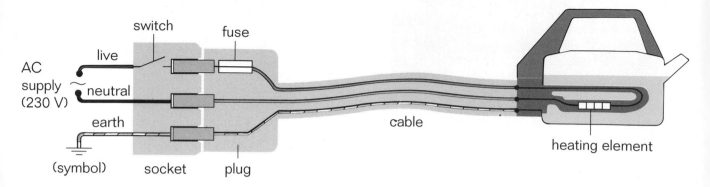

In Britain, the voltage of the AC mains is 230 volts.
Mains *frequency* is 50 hertz (Hz): the alternating current
flows backwards and forwards 50 times per second.

The three-pin plug is wired like this:

Earth wire
(green and yellow insulation)
This is a safety wire. It
stops the metal case of the
kettle becoming 'live' if
something goes wrong.

Radios, TVs, and lamps do
not usually have an earth
wire. But their plastic case
gives extra insulation. They
are *double-insulated*.

Neutral wire
(blue insulation)
This completes the circuit.
It is at zero voltage.

The three 'pins' are made
of brass, a conductor.

The case is made of plastic,
an insulator.

Fuse
This 'blows' if the current
gets too high. A thin piece
of wire overheats, melts,
and breaks the circuit.

Live wire
(brown insulation)
This is at 230 volts AC.

Cable grip
This stops the cable being
pulled out of the plug.

Cable
This has copper wires to
carry the current, with two
layers of flexible plastic
for insulation.

▶ Choosing the right fuse

A plug usually has either a 13 ampere or a 3 ampere fuse in it. The fuse value tells you the current (in amperes) needed to blow the fuse. It should be *higher* than the actual current, but not too high.

Example A 13 ampere fuse is needed for a kettle taking a current of 10 amperes:

A 3 ampere fuse would not be enough. It would blow as soon as you switched on the kettle.

Example A 3 ampere fuse is needed for a TV taking a current of $1/2$ ampere:

A 13 ampere fuse would be too high. If the TV went wrong and took too much current, it might overheat without the fuse blowing.

▶ Safety

·Damaged cables are dangerous. Mains wires need good insulation to stop them touching each other, and to stop anyone touching them.

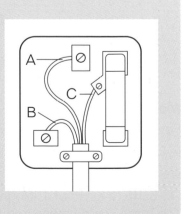

Electric lawnmowers, hedge trimmers, and drills need a safety adaptor like this. It switches off the power if the cable is cut.

---

1 *earth   live   neutral   blue   brown   green and yellow*

   Look at the diagram of the plug on the right. Then copy these sentences and fill in the blanks using the words above:

   A is the ____ wire. Its insulation is ____.
   B is the ____ wire. Its insulation is ____.
   C is the ____ wire. Its insulation is ____.

2 Copy and complete these sentences:
   a If a hairdrier takes a current of 7 amperes, a 3 ampere fuse would not be suitable for it because....
   b If a TV takes a current of 1 ampere, a 13 ampere fuse would not be suitable for it because....

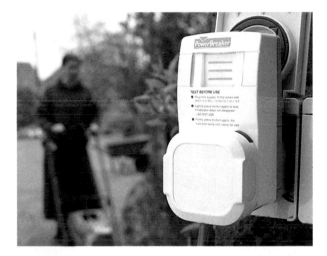

▶ **Forces in action**

A force is a push or pull. Here are some examples of forces:

Friction This gives a tyre grip on the road when the brakes go on. There is more about friction in Spread 4.8.

Tension This is the force in a stretched spring, string, or rope.

Weight This is the downward force of gravity.

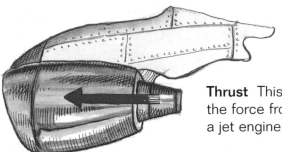

Thrust This is the force from a jet engine.

Air resistance This force tries to slow you down when you are cycling along.

Newtonmeter

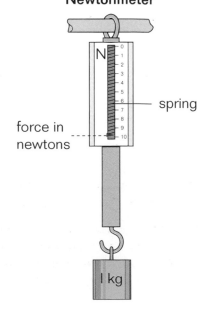

N

spring

force in newtons

1 kg

▶ **Measuring force**

Force is measured in *newtons* (*N*).

Weight is a force. So scientists measure it in newtons, just like any other force.

On Earth, a mass of 1 kilogram has a weight of about 10 newtons. The force can be measured using a *newtonmeter*.

Balanced and unbalanced forces

A skydiver jumps from a helicopter. The forces on her are *air resistance* (upwards) and her *weight* (downwards)......

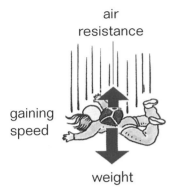

air resistance

gaining speed

weight

At first, the downward force is stronger than the upward force. The forces are **unbalanced**, so the skydiver **accelerates** (gains speed).

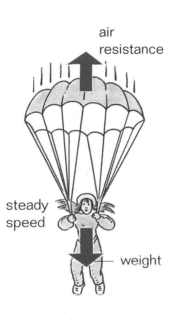

air resistance

steady speed

weight

Now, the forces are equal. They are **balanced**. Neither force wins, so she doesn't speed up, and she doesn't slow down. Her speed is *steady*.

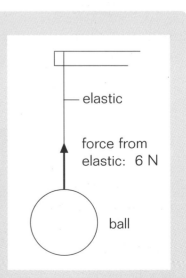

no speed

weight

upward force from ground

Now she is standing on the ground. The ground is compressed. It pushes upwards and supports her weight. The forces are *balanced*.

---

1 Here are five types of force:
friction   air resistance   weight   tension   thrust
Copy these sentences. Fill in the blanks, choosing words from those above.
    The downward force of gravity is called ____.
    The force between a tyre and the road is called ____.
    The force in a stretched rope is called ____.
    The upward force on a falling skydiver is called ____.

2 In the diagram on the right, there is an upward force of 6 N on the ball. Write down what the letter N stands for.

3 Copy the diagram on the right.
Draw in a force arrow for the weight of the ball.
Next to this force arrow, write down the size of the force (for example 1 N or 2 N or some other value - you must decide).

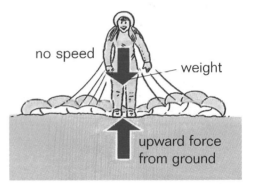

elastic

force from elastic: 6 N

ball

Pressure

You can't push your thumb into wood. But you *can* push a drawing pin in using the same force. That is because the force is concentrated on a much smaller area. Scientists say that the **pressure** is higher.

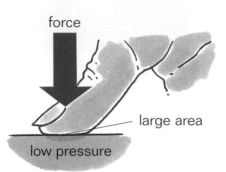

force

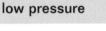

large area

low pressure

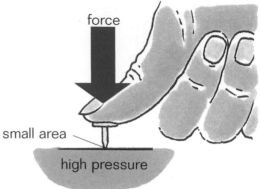

force

small area

high pressure

Spreading the force over a *large area* gives...

low pressure

This ski spreads the skier's weight, so the foot doesn't sink into soft snow.

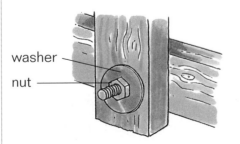

washer

nut

When you tighten the nut, the washer spreads the force, so the nut doesn't go into the wood.

Concentrating the force on a *small area* gives...

high pressure

When the studs on this boot are pressed down, they sink into the ground to give good grip.

A sharp blade concentrates the force so that cutting is easy.

Measuring pressure

Pressure is measured in **newtons per square metre** (**N/m²**).

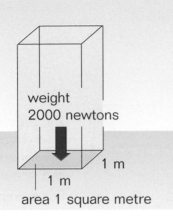

weight
2000 newtons

1 m
1 m
area 1 square metre

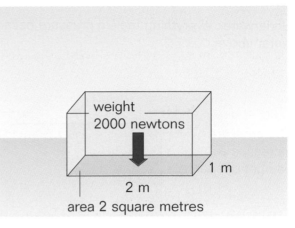

weight
2000 newtons

1 m
2 m
area 2 square metres

This block weighs 2000 newtons. So there is force of 2000 newtons pressing on 1 square metre of ground.

The *pressure* under this block is 2000 newtons per square metre.

This block also weighs 2000 newtons. But it is pressing on 2 square metres of ground. So there is a force of 1000 newtons on *each square metre*.

The *pressure* under this block is only 1000 newtons per square metre.

Tyre pressure gauges are sometimes marked in 'psi' (pounds per square inch).

The pressure in this tyre is 50 psi. That is the same as a pressure of 350 000 newtons per square metre.

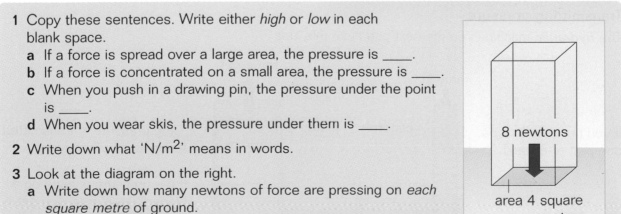

1 Copy these sentences. Write either *high* or *low* in each blank space.
  a If a force is spread over a large area, the pressure is ____.
  b If a force is concentrated on a small area, the pressure is ____.
  c When you push in a drawing pin, the pressure under the point is ____.
  d When you wear skis, the pressure under them is ____.

2 Write down what 'N/m²' means in words.

3 Look at the diagram on the right.
  a Write down how many newtons of force are pressing on *each square metre* of ground.
  b Write down the pressure under the block in N/m².

8 newtons

area 4 square metres

Liquid pressure

Underwater, everything feels a pressure because of the weight of water above.

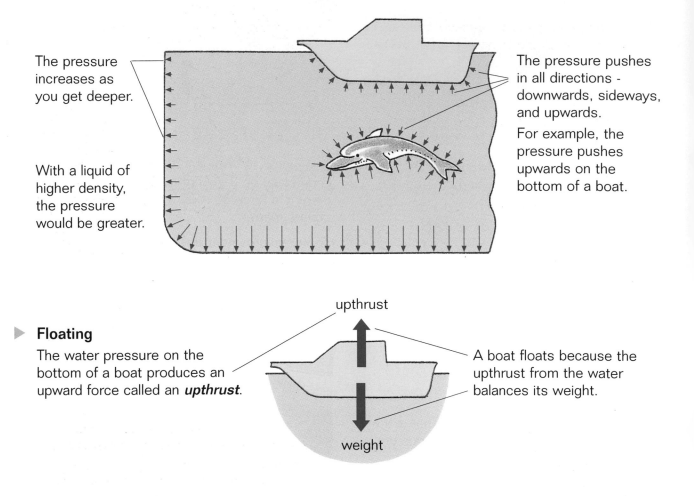

The pressure increases as you get deeper.

With a liquid of higher density, the pressure would be greater.

The pressure pushes in all directions - downwards, sideways, and upwards.

For example, the pressure pushes upwards on the bottom of a boat.

▶ Floating

The water pressure on the bottom of a boat produces an upward force called an **upthrust**.

upthrust

weight

A boat floats because the upthrust from the water balances its weight.

▶ Transmitting pressure

The *hydraulic* machines on the next page use this idea :

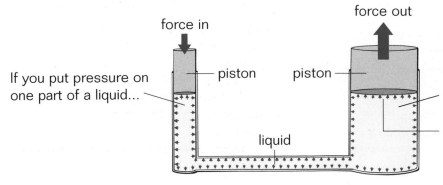

force in

force out

piston   piston

liquid

If you put pressure on one part of a liquid...

...the pressure is transmitted (sent) to all other parts.

If the pressure pushes on a bigger piston area, you get a bigger force out, though the piston does not move as far.

Hydraulic machines

These work using pressurized liquids. Here is one example - the disc brakes on a car:

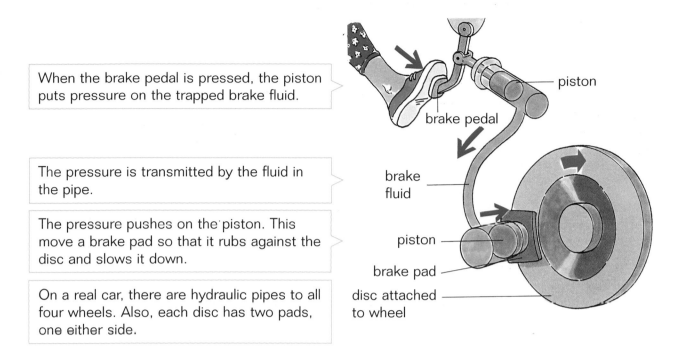

When the brake pedal is pressed, the piston puts pressure on the trapped brake fluid.

The pressure is transmitted by the fluid in the pipe.

The pressure pushes on the piston. This move a brake pad so that it rubs against the disc and slows it down.

On a real car, there are hydraulic pipes to all four wheels. Also, each disc has two pads, one either side.

This digger uses hydraulics to move its shovel. How many pistons can you see in the picture?

1 Copy these sentences in the correct order to show how the car brakes in the diagram above work.

  The piston moves a pad against a disc.
  The fluid transmits the pressure.
  The pressure pushes on a piston.
  The piston puts pressure on a fluid.
  The brake pedal pushes on a piston.

2 Copy and complete these sentences:
  a As you go deeper into water, the pressure....
  b In a liquid, the pressure doesn't just push downwards, it pushes....
  c A boat floats because its weight is balanced by....
  d To transmit forces, hydraulic machines use....

Turning forces

Forces can make things turn. They can have a turning effect.

On the right, someone is using a spanner to turn a bolt. The force has a turning effect on the bolt.

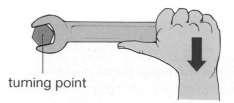

turning point

Here are two ways of making the turning effect *twice* as strong:

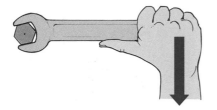 

Pull with *twice* the force.   Use a spanner *twice* as long.

▶ **Balance**

The people below are sitting on the see-saw so that it balances.

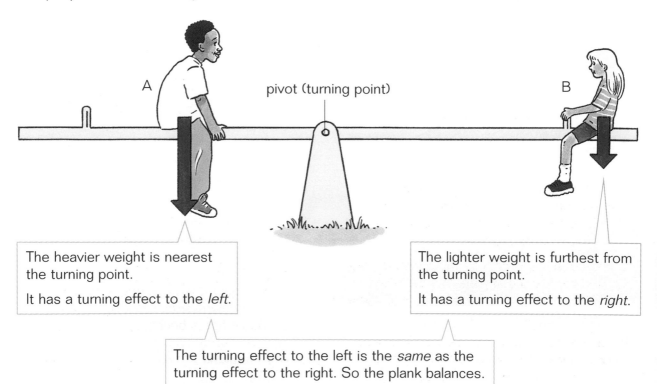

A

pivot (turning point)

B

The heavier weight is nearest the turning point.

It has a turning effect to the *left*.

The lighter weight is furthest from the turning point.

It has a turning effect to the *right*.

The turning effect to the left is the *same* as the turning effect to the right. So the plank balances.

▶ Centre of gravity

Every part of your body weighs something. Together, all these tiny forces act like a single force, your **weight**. This is at a point called your **centre of gravity**.

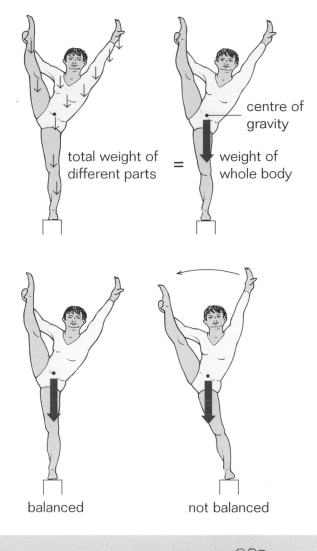

total weight of different parts = weight of whole body

centre of gravity

To balance like this, you have to keep your centre of gravity over the beam. Otherwise your weight will have a turning effect and pull you over.

balanced   not balanced

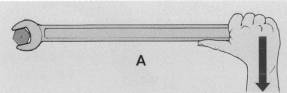

A   B   force

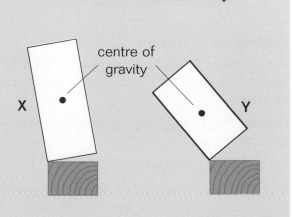

centre of gravity

X   Y

1 Look at spanner A and spanner B above. Then copy and complete this sentence:
   Spanner __ has the stronger turning effect on the nut because......

2 Look at the see-saw on the opposite page. Then copy and complete this sentence:
   To balance the see-saw, person B must be furthest from the pivot because......

3 Look at block X and block Y on the right. Then copy and complete this sentence:
   Block __ will tip over because........

4.12 Moving and stopping

▶ Speed

The cyclist in the photograph has a *speed* of.....

15 metres per second

This means that the cyclist will move 15 metres along the track in one second.

Here are some speeds in miles per hour ('mph'), changed into metres per second:

 mph  mph

13 metres per second   31 metres per second

▶ Friction

This is the force that tries to stop things sliding past each other.
It can be a problem........   ......but it can be useful.

Friction makes it difficult to drag a sledge over the ground.

Friction gives your hands grip on the rope.

Friction gives your shoes grip on the ground.

▶ Getting rid of friction

In machinery, friction slows the moving parts and makes them hot. These things help get rid of friction:

Grease This is very slippery. It helps metal parts slide easily.

Oil is also very slippery.

Ball bearings These roll round so that a wheel does not rub against its shaft.

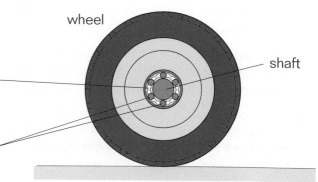

wheel

shaft

Smooth shape

Air resistance is a type of friction. It slows cars down and wastes fuel.

For less air resistance, a car needs a smooth shape so that it slips through the air more easily.

▶ Friction on a bicycle

Friction is a problem:

Air resistance This slows you down. With the wind against you, it slows you even more.

Bearings The wheels spin round on these. Any friction here slows you down.

Friction is useful:

Saddle Friction stops you sliding about.

Handlebar grips Without friction, your hands would slip.

Brakes When rubber blocks press against the wheels, friction slows the wheels down.

Pedals Friction stops your feet slipping.

Tyres Friction lets the tyres grip the road. Without friction, it would be like riding on ice.

---

1 Copy these sentences. Put a word or number in each blank:
   A car has a ___ of 20 metres per second.
   In 1 second, the car will move ___ metres.
   In 2 seconds, the car will move ___ metres.

2 Copy the table on the right. Fill in each blank to show whether the friction is *useful* or a *problem*. The first one has been done for you.

3 Look at the cyclist and bicycle in the photograph on the opposite page. Make a list of all the features which help get rid of friction (air resistance is a type of friction).

Example of friction	Friction: *useful* or a *problem*
Walking on ground	useful
Gripping handlebars	
Machinery going round	
Climbing a rope	
Skating on ice	
Putting on brakes	

4.13 Energy

You spend *energy* when you climb the stairs, lift a bag, or hit a ball. Energy is spent whenever a force makes something move.

Some things store energy.

This energy can be used to make other things move.

▶ Forms of energy

Kinetic energy This is the energy of moving things ('kinetic' means 'moving').

Potential energy This is stored energy. You give something potential energy if you lift it up or stretch it.

Chemical energy Foods, fuels, and batteries store energy in this form. Chemical reactions release the energy.

Heat energy (thermal energy) This comes from hot things when they cool down.

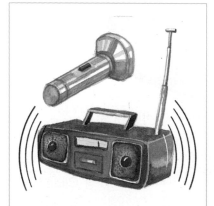

Light energy and **sound energy**

Electrical energy This is the energy carried by an electric current.

Nuclear energy This is energy stored in the nucleus of an atom.

Measuring energy

Energy is measured in *joules* (J).

50 joules

Energy of a football
when you kick it.

300 000 joules

Energy stored in a
chocolate biscuit.

400 000 000
000 000 000
000 000 000
joules

Energy leaving the Sun
every second.

Energy chains

When you spend money, it doesn't vanish.
Someone else spends it, then someone
else..... and so on.

When you spend energy, it doesn't vanish. It
changes into a different form, then a different
form.......and so on, in an *energy chain*:

Law of conservation of energy

This law says:

*Energy can change into different forms,
but you cannot make energy and you
cannot destroy it.*

| chemical energy | → | kinetic energy | → | potential energy | → | kinetic energy | → | heat energy |

The body gets this
energy from food.

When things bang or rub
together, they heat up.

1 *kilograms   joules   forms*

Copy and complete these sentences, choosing
words from those above.
   Energy is measured in ____.
   Energy can change into different ____, but it
   never vanishes.

2 Copy the table on the right. In each blank space,
write in an example of something with that form
of energy. The first one has been done for you.

Form of energy	Example
light	torch beam
kinetic	
chemical	
potential	

Storing and changing energy

▶ Heat and temperature

A high temperature isn't the same as lots of heat energy:

The sparks from this sparkler are at 1600 °C. But they hold so little heat energy, that they don't burn you when they touch your skin.

This molten (melted) iron is also at 1600 °C. It holds lots of heat energy, and is far too dangerous to touch.

▶ Energy storers

Some things are useful because they store energy:

In this toy, a spring stores energy when you wind it up. When it unwinds, it releases the energy and moves the toy.

This battery stores energy when you connect it to a charger. It delivers the energy as an electric current.

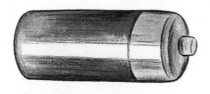

A hot water bottle stores enough energy to keep your feet warm for about an hour.

This battery isn't rechargeable. It is made from chemicals which already store energy.

Storing the Sun's energy

Plants take in energy from sunlight (see Spread 2.2).

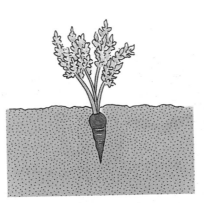

The energy is stored in roots and leaves as they grow.

Animals (like us) can get this energy by eating plants.

Energy changers

Some things are useful because they change energy into a different form:

An electric kettle changes......electrical energy...  ...into heat energy.

A loudspeaker changes..........electrical energy...  ...into sound energy.

A gas ring changes................chemical energy... ...into heat energy.

---

1 Copy these sentences. Write TRUE or FALSE after each one:

A kettleful of boiling water has the same temperature as a cupful of boiling water, but it holds more heat energy.

If something has a high temperature, it must have lots of heat energy.

2 *hairdrier   plant   candle   hot water bottle*

Copy and complete these sentences, choosing words from those above.

A ____ stores heat energy.

A ____ stores energy from the Sun.

A ____ changes electrical energy into heat energy.

A ____ changes chemical energy into heat energy.

Heat on the move

Here are two ways in which heat can move:

▶ ## Conduction

If you heat one end of a metal bar, the atoms vibrate more quickly. Soon, their extra energy is passed to atoms all along the bar. Heat is moving through the bar by *conduction*. The metal is a good *conductor* of heat.

Poor conductors of heat are called *insulators*.

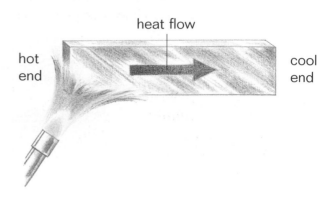

heat flow

hot end

cool end

Good conductors	Insulators (poor conductors)	

metals
  especially
  silver
  copper
  aluminium
	glass
	water
	plastic
	wood
	materials with air trapped in them
	air
		wool
		fibrewool
		plastic foam
		fur
		feathers

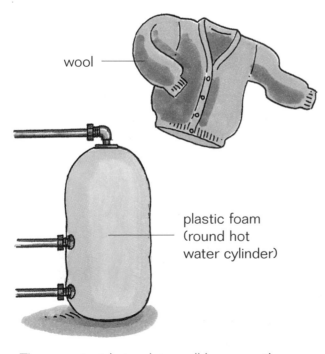

wool

plastic foam (round hot water cylinder)

These materials insulate well because they have air trapped in them. Air is an insulator.

Fluffed-up feathers insulate well because they trap air.

Convection

When air is heated, it rises. Cool air moves in to take its place. This sets up a flow of air called a **convection current**. Other gases and liquids can also have convection currents in them.

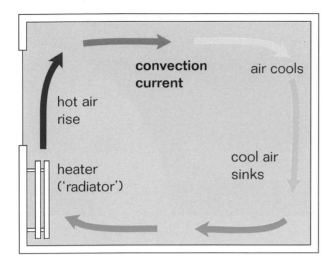

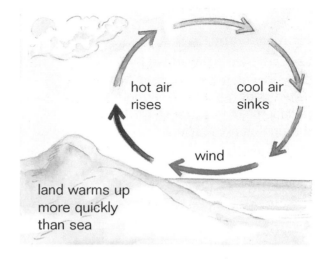

Most rooms are heated by convection. Hot air rises above a 'radiator'. This sets up a convection current which carries heat to all parts of the room.

Convection makes winds blow near the coast. During the day, the land warms up more quickly than the sea. As hot air rises above the land, cool air blows in from the sea.

1 Copy and complete these sentences:
   Poor conductors of heat are called....
   Wool is a good insulator because....

2 *silver   glass   copper   wood*
   air   plastic foam   aluminium

   Write out the materials above in two lists, one headed 'Good conductors' and the other headed 'Insulators'.

3 Write down *two* examples of heat insulators used in clothing.

4 Write down *two* examples of heat insulators used in the home.

5 *convection   conduction   hot   cool*

   Copy the diagram on the right. Fill in the blanks, choosing words from those above.

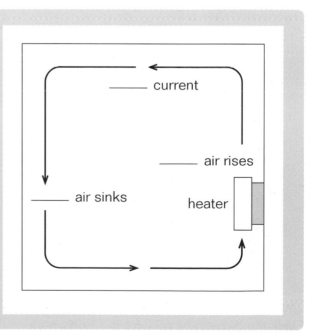

More heat on the move

This spread tells you about two more ways in which heat can move.

▶ **Heat radiation**

On Earth, we are warmed by the Sun. The rays that warm us are called *heat radiation* (thermal radiation). They travel to Earth through empty space.

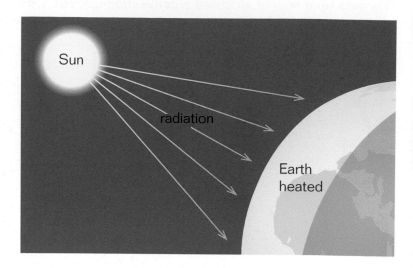

All hot things give off heat radiation. But some surfaces are better at giving it off than others.

Giving off radiation

best -------------------- worst

dull black	shiny black	white	shiny and light

When heat radiation strikes something, it may be *reflected* (bounced off) or *absorbed* (taken in).

Reflecting radiation

worst -------------------- best

Absorbing radiation

best -------------------- worst

On a sunny day, a white car is cooler than a black car because it reflects the Sun's rays.

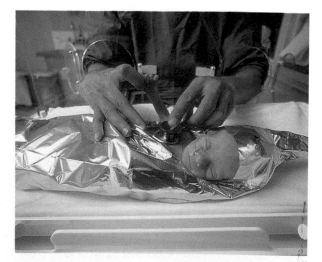

This shiny bag helps keep the premature baby warm.

Thermos flask This can keep a drink hot for hours. The heat escapes very slowly:

Shiny surfaces cut down the heat lost by **radiation**.

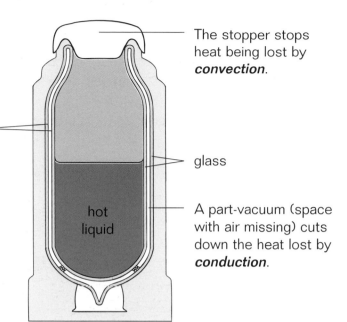

The stopper stops heat being lost by **convection**.

glass

hot liquid

A part-vacuum (space with air missing) cuts down the heat lost by **conduction**.

Evaporation

Wet hands dry out in a few minutes. This is because the water **evaporates** (changes into vapour). If air is blowing from a drier, the water evaporates much faster.

As your hands dry, they feel colder. This is because heat is needed to turn water into vapour (see Spread 3.2). The vapour takes the heat from your hands, so they cool down.

1 Copy and complete these sentences by writing MORE or LESS in each blank space.
   a A white kettle loses heat ____ quickly than a black kettle.
   b A white car reflects ____ of the Sun's rays than a black car.
   c A white car absorbs ____ of the Sun's rays than a black car.
   d If air blows over wet hands, the water evaporates ____ quickly.

2 Choose the word on the right that which goes with each of these. (You can use the same word more than once.)
   a Heat reaches us from the Sun like this.
   b A flask is shiny so that less heat is lost like this.
   c A flask needs a stopper to stop heat being lost like this.

conduction

convection

radiation

Energy for electricity

Our homes and factories need energy. Much of it is supplied by electricity. The electricity comes from **power stations**.

In a power station, the electric power is produced by a **generator**:

shaft

generator

cables

When this is turned.. ..power comes out here.

Turbine

▶ **Inside a power station**

Most large power stations work like this:

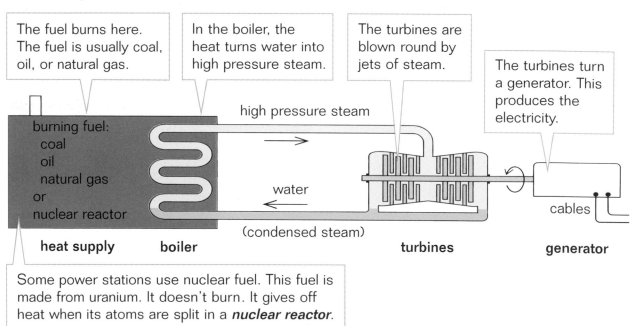

The fuel burns here. The fuel is usually coal, oil, or natural gas.

In the boiler, the heat turns water into high pressure steam.

The turbines are blown round by jets of steam.

The turbines turn a generator. This produces the electricity.

high pressure steam

burning fuel:
coal
oil
natural gas
or
nuclear reactor

water

(condensed steam)

cables

heat supply   **boiler**   **turbines**   **generator**

Some power stations use nuclear fuel. This fuel is made from uranium. It doesn't burn. It gives off heat when its atoms are split in a **nuclear reactor**.

Pollution When a power station burns fuel, its chimney gives out invisible waste gases.

Carbon dioxide adds to global warming (the greenhouse effect).

Sulphur dioxide mainly comes from coal-burning power stations. It causes acid rain.

Turning the generators

In the power station on the opposite page, the generator was turned by steam.

Here are some other ways of turning generators. None of them make polluting gases:

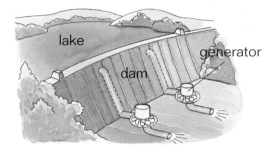

Hydroelectric power River and rainwater fill up a lake behind a dam. Water rushes down from the lake and turns the generators.

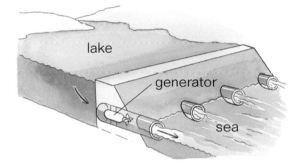

Tidal power The dam is across a river where it meets the sea. The lake fills when the tide comes in. It empties when the tide goes out. The flow of water turns the generators.

Wind power Huge windmills are blown round by the wind. There is a generator in each windmill.

1 Copy these sentences in the correct order so that they describe what happens inside a fuel-burning power station:
> The turbines turn a generator.
> The heat is used to make steam in a boiler.
> The burning fuel gives off heat.
> The generator produces electricity.
> Jets of steam blow the turbines round.

2 Five types of power station are listed on the right.
Copy and complete these sentences. (You have to write in the types of power station which go with each one. You can choose the same type more than once.)
> The power stations that produce waste gases are....
> The power stations that do not produce waste gases are....
> The power stations that use the force of flowing water are....

Power stations
fuel–burning
nuclear
tidal
wind
hydroelectric

4.18 Energy supplies

▶ **Energy from the Sun**

Plants get their energy from the Sun.

Like other animals, we get our energy by eating plants - or by eating animals which have fed on plants. So all the energy for our bodies comes from the Sun.

energy

▶ **Fossil fuels**

Our main fuels are oil, natural gas, and coal. These are called *fossil fuels*. They formed from the remains of plants and tiny sea creatures that lived millions of years ago. So they store energy which once came from the Sun.

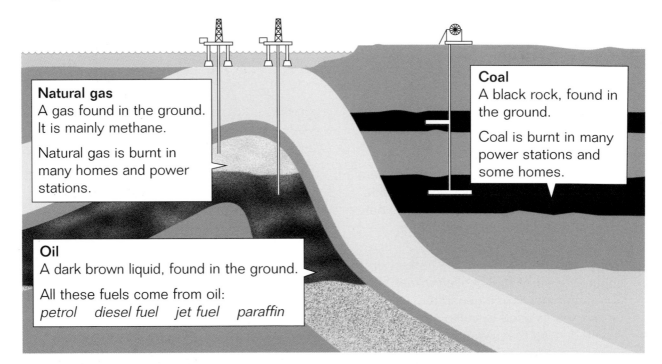

Natural gas
A gas found in the ground. It is mainly methane.

Natural gas is burnt in many homes and power stations.

Coal
A black rock, found in the ground.

Coal is burnt in many power stations and some homes.

Oil
A dark brown liquid, found in the ground.

All these fuels come from oil:
petrol   diesel fuel   jet fuel   paraffin

Our supplies of fossil fuels will not last for ever. The chart shows how many years they will last if we go on using them at the present rate.

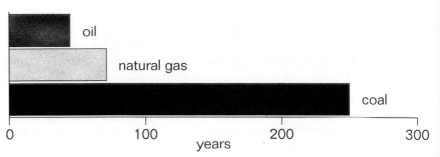

oil

natural gas

coal

| 0 | 100 | 200 | 300 |

years

Biofuels

These are fuels made from plants, or from plant and animal waste. Here are some examples:

Wood is the main fuel for many people in the world.

Alcohol can be made from sugar cane. In some countries, cars use it instead of petrol.

Methane gas comes from the rotting waste in rubbish tips and sewage works.

Renewable or non-renewable?

Some energy supplies are *renewable*. They never run out because they can always be replaced.

For example
You can grow more trees to replace those cut down.

Renewable energy supplies

Examples
hydroelectric energy
tidal energy
wind energy
biofuels

Non-renewable energy supplies

Examples
fossil fuels:
    coal
    oil
    natural gas
nuclear fuel

Some energy supplies are *non-renewable*. Once they have run out, they cannot be replaced.

For example
Oil can't be replaced. It takes too long to form in the ground.

---

1 Copy these sentences in the correct order so that they describe how the energy in our bodies came from the Sun.
    Food energy is stored and used in our bodies.
    Humans eat plants.
    Plants take in energy from sunlight.
    The Sun radiates energy.
    Plants store energy in their roots and leaves.

2 Copy the table on the right.
    Write *yes* or *no* in each blank space to show whether each fuel is a fossil fuel or not, and whether it is renewable or not. One example has been done for you.

Fuel	Fossil fuel?	Renewable?
wood	no	
coal		
alcohol		
oil		
natural gas		

How the world gets its energy

Solar panels
These use the Sun's rays to heat water for the house.

Solar cells
These use the energy in sunlight to produce electricity.

The Sun
Deep inside the Sun, atoms change their nuclear energy into heat. The Sun radiates more energy than a million billion billion electric fires!

Energy in food
Our bodies get energy from food. The food may be from plants, or from animals which have fed on plants.

Energy in plants
Plants take in energy from sunlight. The energy is stored in their leaves and roots as they grow.

Biofuels from plants
Biofuels are fuels from plants and other 'living' materials. Wood is a biofuel. Alcohol is a biofuel made from sugar cane.

Fossil fuels
The main fossil fuels are oil, natural gas, and coal. They formed from the remains of plants and animals that lived millions of years ago. Power stations, factories, and vehicles burn fossil fuels.

Biofuels from waste
Methane gas comes from rotting waste and sewage. It can be burnt as a fuel. Waste paper and other rubbish can also be burnt as a fuel.

Batteries
Batteries store energy. Some are given energy by charging them with electricity. Others are made from chemicals that already store energy.

Fuels from oil
Petrol, diesel fuel, jet fuel, paraffin, central heating oil, bottled gas.

The Moon
The Moon's gravity pulls on the oceans and makes them bulge. As the Earth turns, each place has a high and low tide as it moves in and out of a bulge.

Tidal energy
As the tide comes in and goes out, the flow of water turns generators.

The atom
Some atoms have lots of nuclear energy stored in them. Changes in these atoms can release this energy.

Nuclear energy
In a nuclear reactor, uranium atoms release energy as heat. The heat is used to make steam for driving generators.

Geothermal energy
Deep underground, the rocks are very hot. The heat comes from radioactive atoms. It can be used to make steam for heating buildings or driving generators.

The weather
The Sun's heat makes winds blow across the Earth. It lifts water vapour from the oceans. Later, the water falls as rain.

Wave energy
Waves are caused by winds and tides. The up-and-down movement of the water can be used to drive generators.

Hydroelectric energy
Water rushes down from a lake and turns generators. Rainwater keeps the lake topped up.

Wind energy
For centuries, sailing ships have used the power of the wind. Today, huge windmills can turn generators.

Making sounds

▶ Sound waves

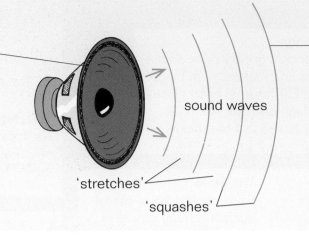

When a loudspeaker cone vibrates, it stretches and squashes the air in front.

sound waves

'stretches'

'squashes'

The 'stretches' and 'squashes' spread through the air like ripples on a pond. They are **sound waves**. In your ears, you hear them as sound.

▶ Features of sound

Sound needs something to move through

Sound waves can travel through gases, liquids, and solids. But they cannot travel through a vacuum (empty space).

The air has been taken out of this jar, so you cannot hear the alarm clock.

Sound is made by vibrations

Here are some things that give out sound waves when they vibrate:

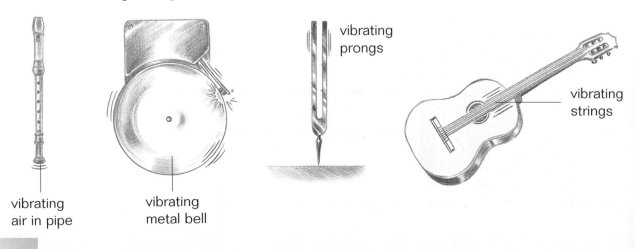

vibrating air in pipe

vibrating metal bell

vibrating prongs

vibrating strings

The speed of sound

In air, the speed of sound is about 330 metres per second. This means that sound travels the length of three football pitches in a second:

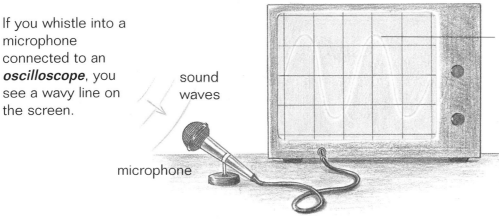

The speed of light is 300 000 *kilo*metres per second. So light is much faster than sound. That is why you see a flash of lightning before you hear it.

Sound on screen

oscilloscope

If you whistle into a microphone connected to an **oscilloscope**, you see a wavy line on the screen.

sound waves

The wavy line is a graph. It shows you how the air next to the microphone vibrates backwards and forwards as time goes on.

microphone

1 Here are some words connected with sound:
    oscilloscope   vacuum   air   vibrations
    Write down the word that matches each of these clues.
    a Sound can travel through this.
    b Sound cannot travel through this.
    c This instrument shows sound waves as a wavy line on a screen.
    d Sound is made by these.

2 Copy these sentences and fill in the blanks. (The information you need is somewhere on this page.)
        The speed of sound in air is.........
        The speed of light is.........
        You see a lightning flash before you hear it because.........

4.21 Hearing sounds

▶ **The ear**

This is what the ear is like inside:

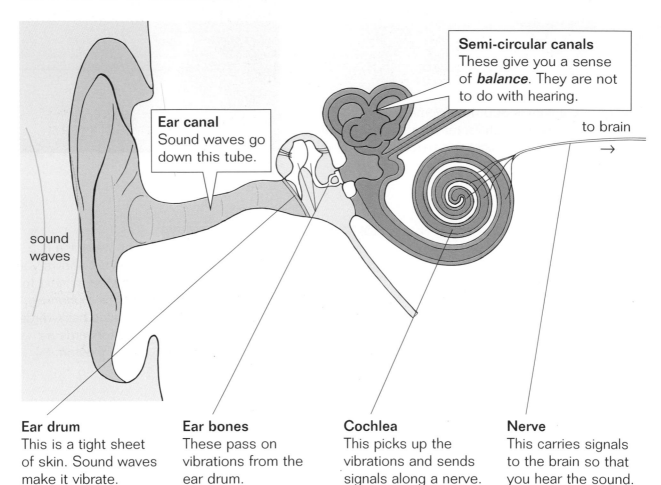

Ear canal
Sound waves go down this tube.

Semi-circular canals
These give you a sense of *balance*. They are not to do with hearing.

to brain
→

sound waves

Ear drum
This is a tight sheet of skin. Sound waves make it vibrate.

Ear bones
These pass on vibrations from the ear drum.

Cochlea
This picks up the vibrations and sends signals along a nerve.

Nerve
This carries signals to the brain so that you hear the sound.

▶ **Low or high**

When you listen to a musical instrument, the note may be

low...   ...or high.

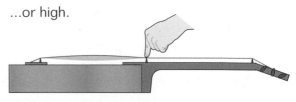

This guitar string is vibrating 200 times every second. So it is sending out 200 sound waves every second. Scientists say that the *frequency* is 200 *hertz* (*Hz*).

This guitar string is vibrating faster: 400 times every second. Its frequency is 400 hertz. To the ear, the note sounds higher than before. The note has a higher *pitch*.

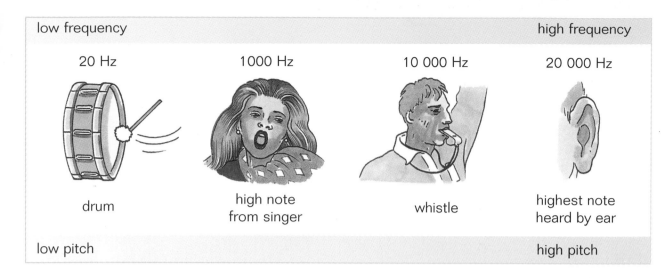

low frequency | high frequency

20 Hz — 1000 Hz — 10 000 Hz — 20 000 Hz

drum | high note from singer | whistle | highest note heard by ear

low pitch | high pitch

▶ Quiet or loud

When you listen to a musical instrument, the note may be

quiet...   ...or loud.

This guitar string is making small vibrations. It is giving out a quiet sound.

This guitar string is making bigger vibrations. It is giving out a louder sound.

▶ Hearing damage

Very loud sounds can damage the cochlea and nerve so that the signals reaching the brain are very weak.

You should never play a personal stereo at high volume. Hours and hours of very loud music will gradually make you go deaf. But the change may be so slow that you do not notice it.

1 Copy these sentences in the correct order so that they describe how the ear works:

    The cochlea sends signals along a nerve to the brain.
    Sound waves go down the ear canal.
    The ear bones pass on the vibrations.
    Sound waves make the ear drum vibrate.
    The vibrations are picked up by the cochlea.

2 *higher   lower   louder   quieter*

Copy these sentences. Fill in the blanks, choosing words from those above:

    If a guitar string vibrates faster, the note becomes ____.
    If the vibrations are bigger, the sound becomes ____.

Reflecting sounds

▶ **Echoes**

Walls and other hard surfaces reflect sound waves:

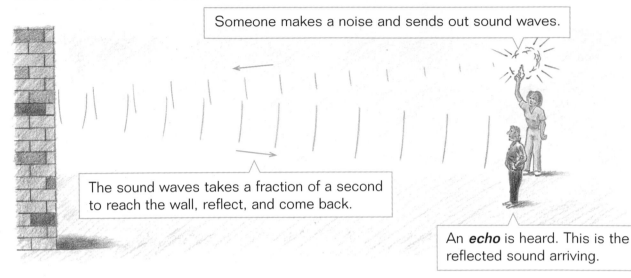

Someone makes a noise and sends out sound waves.

The sound waves takes a fraction of a second to reach the wall, reflect, and come back.

An *echo* is heard. This is the reflected sound arriving.

The speed of sound in air is about 330 metres per second. So..

If the distance to the wall and back is 330 metres....   ....the echo takes 1 second to arrive

If the distance to the wall and back is 660 metres....   ...the echo takes 2 seconds to arrive

▶ **Echo-sounding**

Boats use *echo-sounding* to work out how deep the water is underneath them.

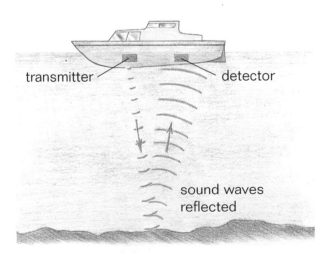

transmitter   detector

sound waves reflected

A burst of sound waves is sent down through the water. The waves reflect from the bottom. The deeper the water, the longer the echo takes to come back.

Bats fly at night. They use echo-sounding to work out where things are in front of them.

The bat gives out a series of clicks (sound pulses). With its big ears, it picks up the echoes. From these, it can tell how far away things are.

▶ Ultrasound

Some sounds are too high for the human ear to hear. Sounds like this are called **ultrasonic** sounds, or **ultrasound**. Bats give out ultrasound. So do the echo-sounders in boats.

Frequency

20 Hz	20 000 Hz	above 20 000 Hz
sounds heard by human ear		ultrasound

In hospitals, ultrasound is used for checking unborn babies in the womb. Ultrasound is safer than X-rays.

The nurse moves an ultrasound transmitter over the mother's body.

The reflected sounds are picked up and analysed by a computer. This puts an image of the baby on the screen.

Inside the womb, the sound waves are reflected by the baby's body.

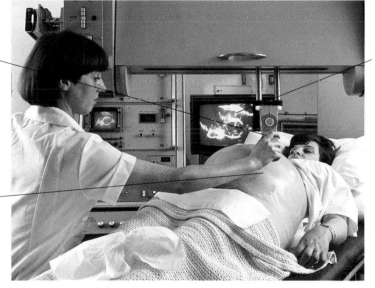

1 *ultrasound   echo   frequency*

   Choose the word above which goes with each of these:
   a A reflected sound.
   b A sound too high for the human ear to hear.

2 Write down *two* uses of ultrasound.

3 Copy and complete these sentences about the boat on the right:
   a The boat is using echo-sounding to find out....
   b If the sound pulses take longer to reflect back from the bottom, this means that the water is.....

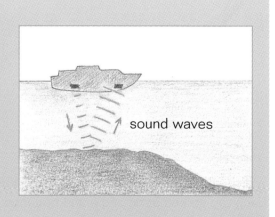

sound waves

173

Rays and mirrors

Light is a form of energy. In space and in air, it travels at a
speed of........

300 000 kilometres *per second* ⟶

Light is the fastest thing there is. It takes less than a millionth
of a second for light to cross a room!

▶ Rays and shadows

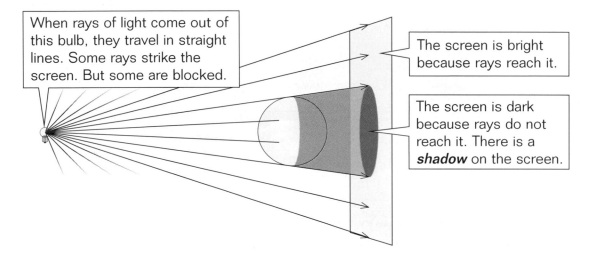

When rays of light come out of
this bulb, they travel in straight
lines. Some rays strike the
screen. But some are blocked.

The screen is bright
because rays reach it.

The screen is dark
because rays do not
reach it. There is a
shadow on the screen.

▶ Reflecting light

You see things if they send light rays into your eyes.

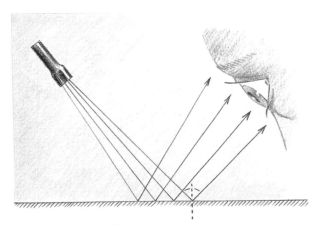

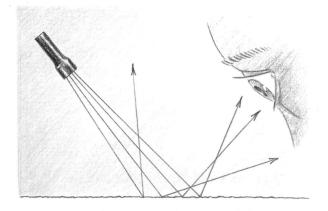

A smooth, shiny surface **reflects** light like this.
Each ray strikes at an angle and bounces off
at the same angle.

A rough surface reflects light all over the
place. You see the surface because some of
the light goes into your eyes.

Image in a mirror

Light rays from this bulb are reflected by the mirror.

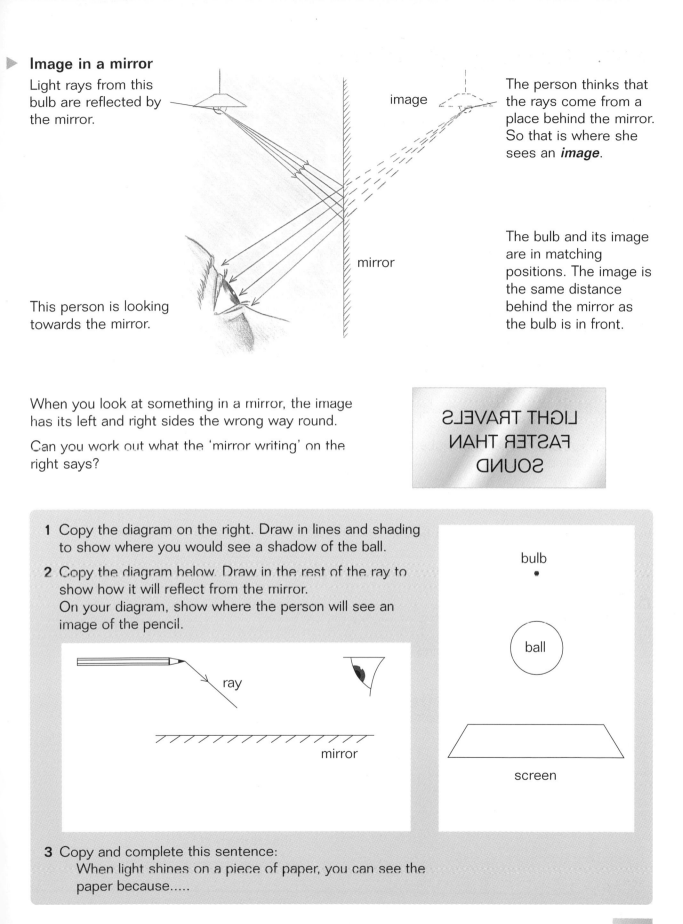

image

mirror

This person is looking towards the mirror.

The person thinks that the rays come from a place behind the mirror. So that is where she sees an *image*.

The bulb and its image are in matching positions. The image is the same distance behind the mirror as the bulb is in front.

When you look at something in a mirror, the image has its left and right sides the wrong way round.

Can you work out what the 'mirror writing' on the right says?

LIGHT TRAVELS FASTER THAN SOUND

1 Copy the diagram on the right. Draw in lines and shading to show where you would see a shadow of the ball.

2 Copy the diagram below. Draw in the rest of the ray to show how it will reflect from the mirror.
On your diagram, show where the person will see an image of the pencil.

ray

mirror

bulb

ball

screen

3 Copy and complete this sentence:
When light shines on a piece of paper, you can see the paper because.....

Bending light

A **transparent** material lets light through, so you can see through it.

Here are some transparent materials:

glass   water   clear plastic

Transparent materials can bend light rays, as well as let them through.

▶ Refraction

The glass block in the photograph is bending light. The bending is called **refraction**.

This ray of light is going into a glass block.

When the light enters the block it bends *towards* this line.

When the light leaves the block, it bends *away* from this line.

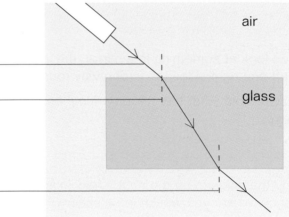

air

glass

▶ Deeper than it looks

This person is looking at a coin on the bottom of a swimming pool.

Light rays from the coin are refracted (bent) when they leave the water....

so the rays seem to come from this position. The person thinks that the coin is here.

The bending effect means that the water looks less deep than it really is.

▶ Why light bends

Here is one explanation:

This roller-skater is moving towards grass. The grass will slow her down.

This skate hits the grass first. So it the first to slow down.

As one skate was slowed before the other, the skater moves in a different direction.

A light beam isn't solid like a skater, but slowing still affects it. When a light beam goes into glass, it slows down and moves in a different direction.

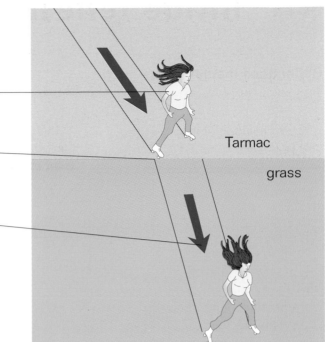

Tarmac

grass

▶ Refraction in air

Light bends when it goes from hot air into cold air - or from cold into hot. That is why you get a wobbly view when hot air is moving about in front of you.

---

1 *reflection   refraction   transparent*
   Copy these sentences. Fill in the blanks, choosing words from those above.
   a If a material is _____, you can see through it.
   b Light bends when it goes into a glass block. The bending is called _____.

2 Copy the diagram on the right.
   Draw in the rest of the ray to show how it goes through the glass block.

3 Copy and complete this sentence:
   When light goes from air into glass, its speed.....

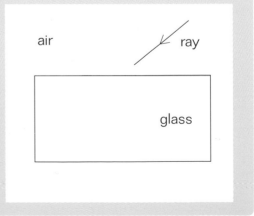

air   ray

glass

Inside reflections

▶ **Reflections inside prisms**

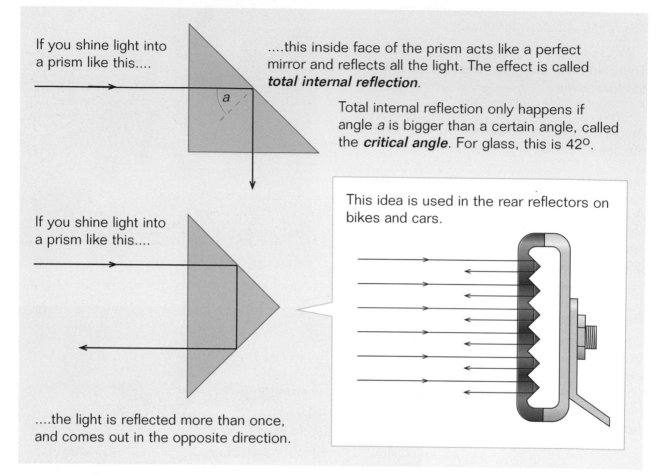

If you shine light into a prism like this....

....this inside face of the prism acts like a perfect mirror and reflects all the light. The effect is called **total internal reflection**.

Total internal reflection only happens if angle *a* is bigger than a certain angle, called the **critical angle**. For glass, this is 42°.

If you shine light into a prism like this....

This idea is used in the rear reflectors on bikes and cars.

....the light is reflected more than once, and comes out in the opposite direction.

▶ **Optical fibres**

Optical fibres are thin strands of glass or plastic. They work using total internal reflection:

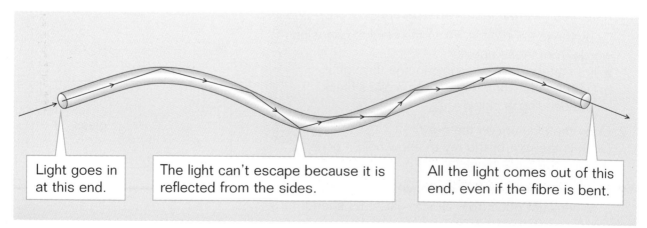

Light goes in at this end.

The light can't escape because it is reflected from the sides.

All the light comes out of this end, even if the fibre is bent.

Using optical fibres

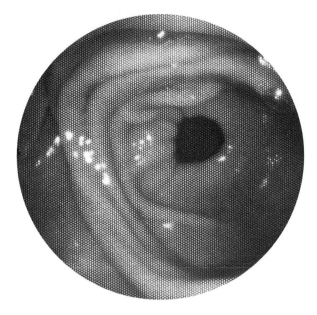

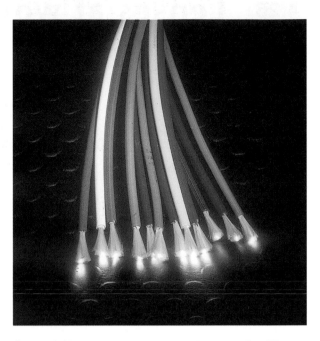

Surgeons can use optical fibres to look inside the body. A thin bundle of fibres is passed into the body. The surgeon looks through an eyepiece and gets a view like the one above.

Optical fibres can carry telephone calls. The sound signals are changed into pulses of laser light. These travel along a fibre. At the far end, they are changed back into sound.

Bundle of fibres

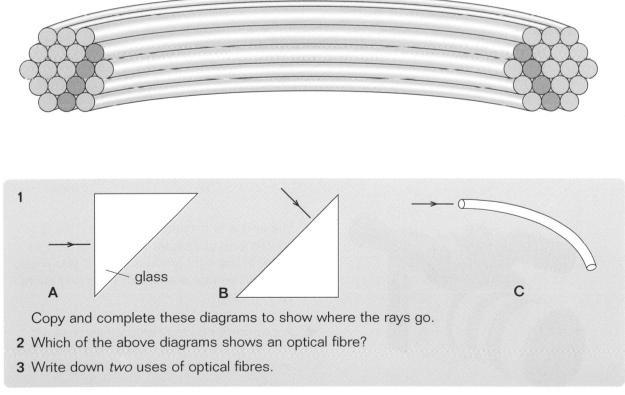

1

A glass

B

C

Copy and complete these diagrams to show where the rays go.

2 Which of the above diagrams shows an optical fibre?

3 Write down *two* uses of optical fibres.

Lenses at work

Lenses bend light and form images. There are two main types:

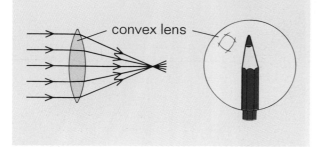

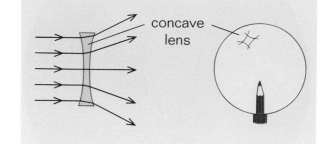

Convex lens This bends light inwards. It makes *very close* things look bigger. A convex lens can be used as a *magnifying glass*.

Concave lens This bends light outwards. It makes things look smaller.

▶ Cameras

With *distant* things, a convex lens brings rays to a *focus*. The rays form a tiny, upside-down image which you can pick up on a screen. This idea is used in a *camera*:

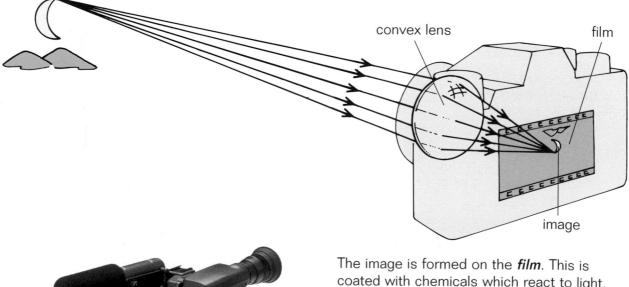

convex lens   film

image

The image is formed on the *film*. This is coated with chemicals which react to light. To let in the right amount of light, you press a button so that a *shutter* opens and shuts very quickly.

◀ A *camcorder* (video camera) also has a convex lens in it. But instead of a film, it has an electronic plate at the back to pick up the image.

The eye

Like a camera, an eye uses a convex lens to form a tiny image at the back.

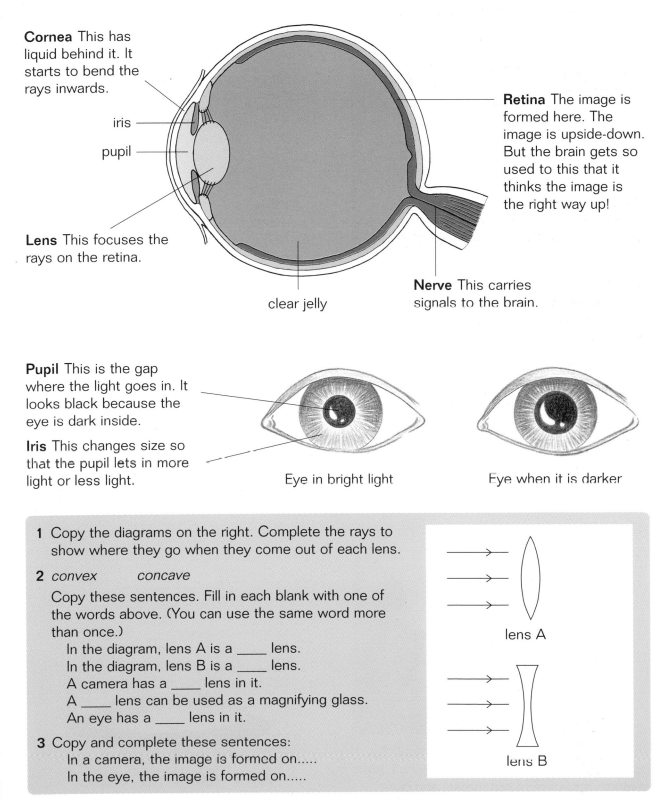

Cornea This has liquid behind it. It starts to bend the rays inwards.

iris

pupil

Lens This focuses the rays on the retina.

Retina The image is formed here. The image is upside-down. But the brain gets so used to this that it thinks the image is the right way up!

clear jelly

Nerve This carries signals to the brain.

Pupil This is the gap where the light goes in. It looks black because the eye is dark inside.

Iris This changes size so that the pupil lets in more light or less light.

Eye in bright light

Eye when it is darker

1 Copy the diagrams on the right. Complete the rays to show where they go when they come out of each lens.

2 *convex*   *concave*

Copy these sentences. Fill in each blank with one of the words above. (You can use the same word more than once.)
  In the diagram, lens A is a ____ lens.
  In the diagram, lens B is a ____ lens.
  A camera has a ____ lens in it.
  A ____ lens can be used as a magnifying glass.
  An eye has a ____ lens in it.

3 Copy and complete these sentences:
  In a camera, the image is formed on.....
  In the eye, the image is formed on.....

lens A

lens B

Seeing colours

▶ A spectrum

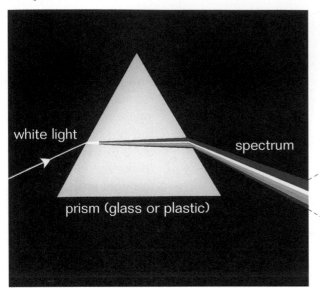

white light

spectrum

prism (glass or plastic)

White light is not a single colour, but a mixture of colours. A **prism** splits them up.

The light is refracted (bent) when it goes into the prism, and when it comes out.

The refracted light spreads to form a range of colours called a **spectrum**:

red
orange
yellow
green
blue
violet

The spreading effect is called **dispersion**.

▶ Making white

The human eye doesn't need all the colours in the spectrum to see white. Red, green, and blue are enough. If beams of red, green, and blue light overlap on a white screen, they make white.

Red, green, and blue are called the **primary colours**.

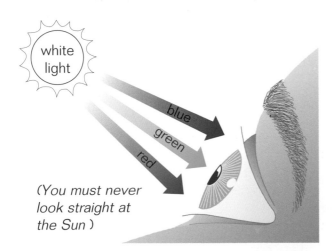

white light

blue

green

red

(You must never look straight at the Sun)

The Sun glows and gives out white light. So does a bulb. To the eye, the white light is the same as a mixture of red, green, and blue.

red   green   blue

red + green + blue = white

Why things look coloured

Most things don't glow. We see them because they reflect light from the Sun or a lamp. However, only some colours may be reflected. The rest are *absorbed* (taken away).

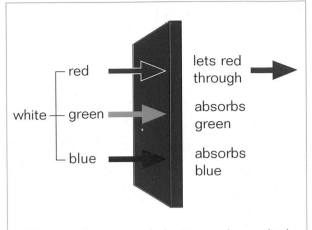

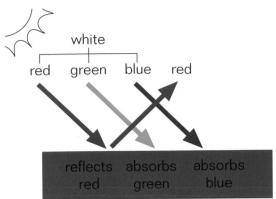

This patch reflects only red light. So it looks red. It absorbs green and blue.

Filters are pieces of plastic or glass which only let some colours through. For example, a red filter lets red light through, but absorbs green and blue.

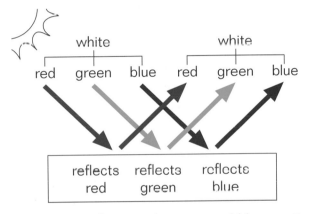

This patch reflects red, green, and blue, so it looks white. It absorbs no colours.

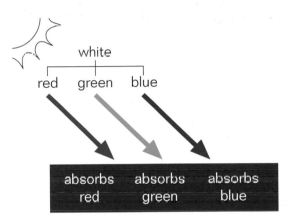

This patch reflects no light, so it looks black. It absorbs red, green, and blue.

---

1 Copy and complete these sentences:
   A triangular glass block is called......
   It can split white light into a range of colours called......

2 On the right, there is a list of colours. Write down the colour or colours which go with each of these statements. (You can choose the same colours more than once.)
   a When white light goes through a prism, this colour is refracted (bent) the least.
   b If these colours overlap on a white screen, they make white.
   c A red filter lets this colour through.
   d If something absorbs all the light striking it, it looks this colour.
   e A red book absorbs these colours.

| white |
| black |
| red |
| green |
| blue |

Electromagnetic radiation

▶ **Light waves**

Light *radiates* (spreads out) from the Sun or a lamp. It is a type of **radiation**.

Light is made up of tiny waves. The waves can't be seen. They are ripples of electric and magnetic force.

Different colours have different **wavelengths**. For example:

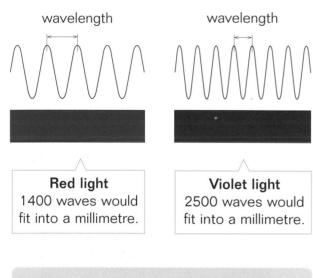

Red light
1400 waves would fit into a millimetre.

Violet light
2500 waves would fit into a millimetre.

The electromagnetic family

Light is part of a big family of waves called **electromagnetic radiation**. This chart shows the different types.

Some microwaves are absorbed by food. This makes the food hot. The idea is used in microwave ovens.

| X-rays | microwaves | ultraviolet |
| infrared | radio waves | gamma rays |

1 One type of electromagnetic radiation is missing from the list above. Which one?

2 List the types of radiation in order, starting with the *longest* wavelength. (Remember to include the missing one!)

3 From your list, choose a type of radiation which matches each of these:
   a Can pass through flesh.
   b Come from radioactive materials.
   c Used for radar.
   d Gives you a sun tan, but can damage your eyes and skin.
   e The only radiation that the eye can see.
   f Used for sending TV signals.
   g Given off by a hot radiator.

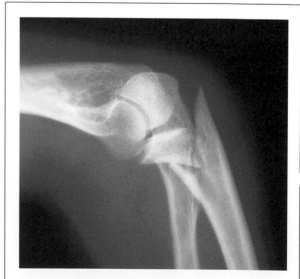

Some X-rays pass through flesh, but not bone. So flesh and bone show up differently on an X-ray photograph.

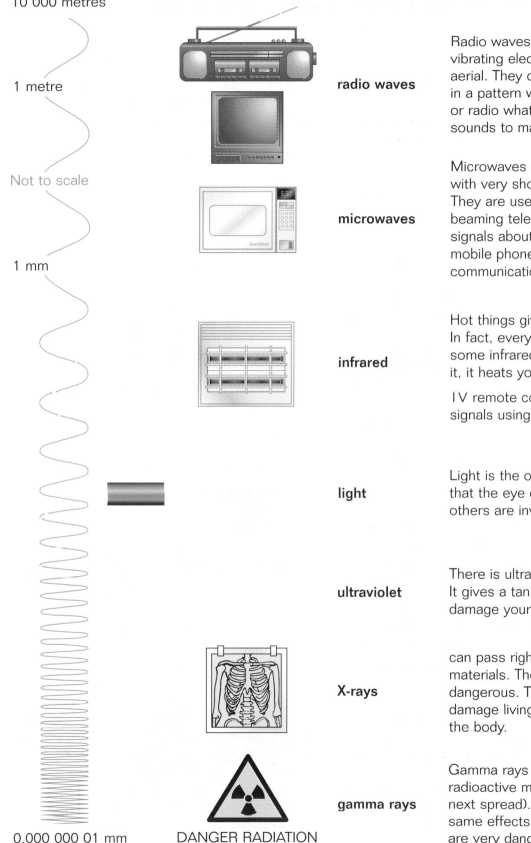

Wavelength:
10 000 metres

1 metre

Not to scale

1 mm

0.000 000 01 mm

radio waves

Radio waves are made by vibrating electricity in an aerial. They can be sent out in a pattern which tells a TV or radio what pictures or sounds to make.

microwaves

Microwaves are radio waves with very short wavelengths. They are used for radar, beaming telephone and TV signals about the country, mobile phones, satellite communication, and cooking.

infrared

Hot things give off infrared. In fact, everything gives off some infrared. If you absorb it, it heats you up.

TV remote controllers send signals using infrared.

light

Light is the only radiation that the eye can see. The others are invisible.

ultraviolet

There is ultraviolet in sunlight. It gives a tan, but can damage your eyes and skin.

X-rays

can pass right through many materials. They are very dangerous. They can damage living cells deep in the body.

gamma rays

Gamma rays come from radioactive materials (see next spread). They have the same effects as X-rays and are very dangerous

DANGER RADIATION

4.29 Radioactivity

Some atoms are *radioactive*. They have unstable nuclei which break up and give out *nuclear radiation*. (For more about the nucleus of an atom, see spread 3.8.)

▶ Types of nuclear radiation

Here are three types of nuclear radiation. They are invisible, but can be detected using a *GM tube* (Geiger-Müller tube):

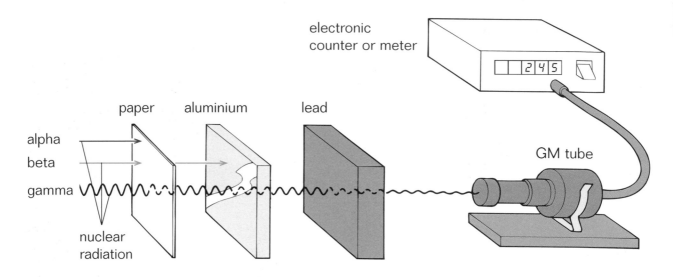

Alpha particles are each made of 2 protons and 2 neutrons. They have positive (+) charge. They can be stopped by thick paper or skin.

Beta particles are electrons. They have a negative (−) charge. They can be stopped by thick aluminium.

Gamma rays are tiny waves like X-rays. They can pass through lead, but it cuts down their strength.

▶ Giving out nuclear radiation

Here are some of the things which give out nuclear radiation:

Rocks and soil have tiny amounts of natural radioactivity in them.

Radon gas is radioactive. Small amounts seep from the ground and can collect in houses.

Nuclear power stations use radioactive fuel. They have thick concrete to stop the radiation getting out.

▶ Dangers of nuclear radiation

Nuclear radiation is harmful. It can damage or kill the cells in living things. In humans and other animals, it can cause cancer. Radioactive gas and dust are very dangerous because they can get deep into the body with the air, food, or water you take in.

DANGER
RADIATION

▶ Weakening radiation

As time goes, on the amount of radiation from a radioactive material gets less and less - though it never completely vanishes.

The age of some rocks can be worked out by measuring how much radiation is still coming from them.

▶ Using nuclear radiation

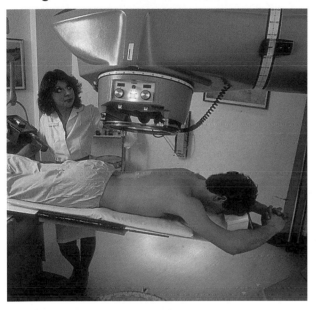

This person is getting **radiotherapy** treatment. A narrow beam of gamma rays is being used to kill cancer cells.

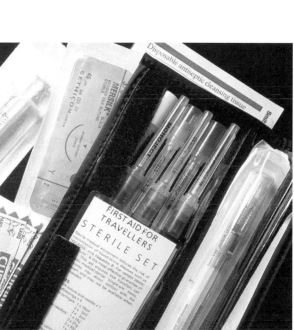

These hypodermic needles were **sterilized** by gamma rays. The rays killed any germs on the needles before they were packed.

1 The things on the right are all linked with radioactivity.
   Write down which one goes with each of the following.
   (You can use the same answer more than once.)
   a This is given out by radioactive materials.
   b This is used to detect nuclear radiation.
   c These are like X-rays.
   d These have a positive (+) charge.
   e These can be stopped by thick paper.
   f These can pass through lead.
   g In hospitals, these are used to kill cancer cells.

   alpha particles
   nuclear radiation
   gamma rays
   GM tube

2 Copy and complete this sentence:
   Nuclear radiation is dangerous because.......

Sun and Earth

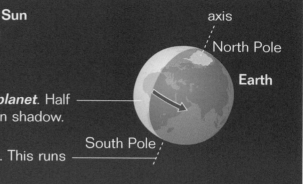

The Sun is a huge, hot, glowing ball of gas called a *star*. It doesn't look very big because it is 150 million kilometres away from us.

The Earth is a much smaller, cooler ball called a *planet*. Half of the Earth is in sunlight, while the other half is in shadow.

The Earth slowly turns about a line called its *axis*. This runs from the North Pole to the South Pole.

Sun axis North Pole Earth South Pole

▶ **Day and night**

The Earth takes **one day** (24 hours) to turn once on its axis. As it turns, places move from the sunlit half into the shadow half. So they move from daytime into night.

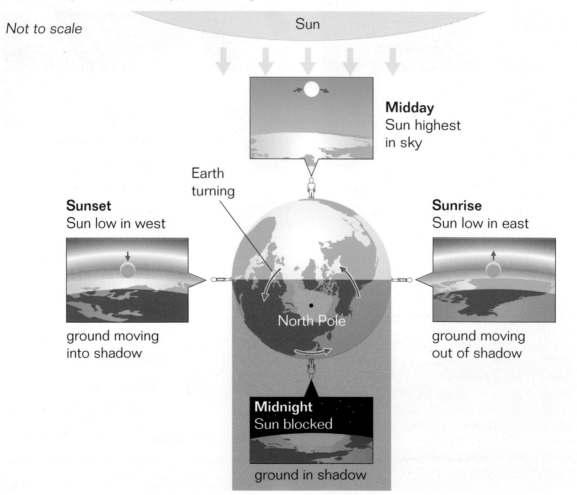

Not to scale

Sun

Midday
Sun highest in sky

Earth turning

Sunset
Sun low in west

ground moving into shadow

North Pole

Sunrise
Sun low in east

ground moving out of shadow

Midnight
Sun blocked

ground in shadow

The year and seasons

The Earth moves around the Sun in a big circle called an **orbit**.
The Earth takes **one year** (about 365 days) to orbit the Sun.

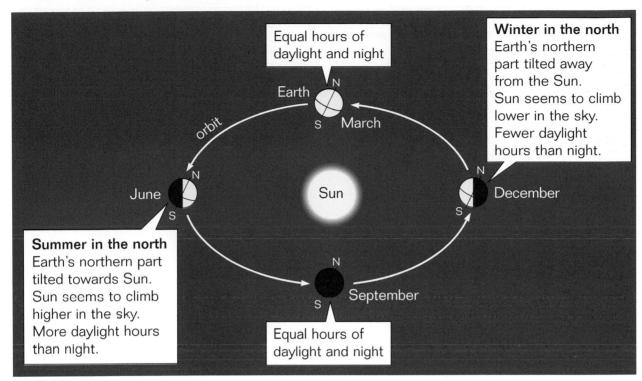

Equal hours of daylight and night

Earth

March

Winter in the north
Earth's northern part tilted away from the Sun. Sun seems to climb lower in the sky. Fewer daylight hours than night.

orbit

June

Sun

December

Summer in the north
Earth's northern part tilted towards Sun. Sun seems to climb higher in the sky. More daylight hours than night.

September

Equal hours of daylight and night

The Earth's axis leans by about 23°. This means that the Earth's northern part is sometimes tilted towards the Sun and sometimes away from it.

In June, the Earth's northern part is tilted towards the Sun. That is when the Sun seems to climb highest in the sky and there are most hours of daylight. So it is summer.

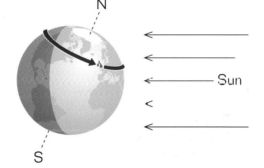

Sun

1 *24 hours*   *7 days*   *365 days*

Copy these sentences. Fill in the blanks, choosing times from those above. (You can use the same time more than once.)

There are ____ in one day.
There are about ____ in one year.
The Earth takes about ____ to orbit the Sun.
The Earth takes ____ to turn once on its axis.

2 a Copy the diagram on the right. Shade in the part of the Earth that is in shadow.

b Write down whether it is *daytime* or *night* in Britain.

c Write down whether it is *summer* or *winter* in Britain.

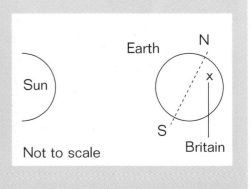

Sun

Earth

N

x

S

Britain

Not to scale

Orbiting the Earth

▶ Satellites in orbit

There are hundreds of satellites in orbit around the Earth.
Here are some of the jobs they do:

Communications satellites These pass on TV and telephone signals.

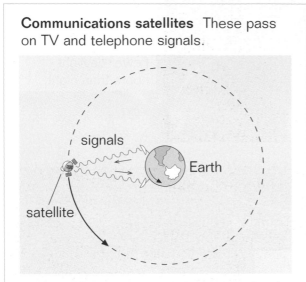

This satellite is in a *geostationary* orbit. It goes round at the same rate as the Earth turns. So it always seems to stay in the same place in the sky.

Weather satellites These send pictures down to Earth so that forecasters can see what the weather is doing.

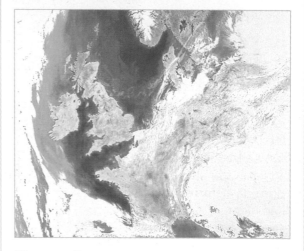

This satellite picture shows the weather over Europe.

Research satellites Some of these carry telescopes for looking at stars and planets. Above the atmosphere, they get a much clearer view.

This is the Hubble Space Telescope. It radios its pictures back to Earth.

Navigation satellites These send out signals so that a ship or aircraft can work out its position.

This receiver picks up signals from satellites, calculates its position, and shows the result.

The Moon

The Moon orbits the Earth. It is smaller than the Earth, and has a rocky surface with lots of craters.

The Moon is *not* hot and glowing like the Sun.

We can only see the Moon because its surface reflects sunlight. We don't see the part that is in shadow.

The Moon takes about 28 days to orbit the Earth.

The Moon takes the same time (28 days) to turn once on its axis. So it always keeps the same face toward the Earth.

The Moon is 380 000 kilometres from Earth. On the diagram, the Moon's orbit ought to be ten times bigger, but there isn't space to show it.

Earth

Moon

1 7   28   365   380 000

Copy these sentences. Fill in the blanks, choosing numbers from those above. (You can use the same number more than once.)

The Moon is ____ kilometres from Earth.

The Moon takes about ____ days to orbit the Earth.

The Moon takes about ____ days to turn once on its axis.

2 *Earth   Moon   Sun*

Copy these sentences. Fill in the blanks, choosing words from those above. (You can use the same word more than once.)

a We see the ____ because it is hot and glowing.

b We see the ____ because it reflects light which came from the ____.

3 Write down *three* jobs that satellites are used for.

4.32 The Solar System

The Sun has lots of *planets* orbiting it. The Sun and its planets are called the **Solar System**.

This diagram shows how the sizes of the Sun and planets compare (the distances are not correct):

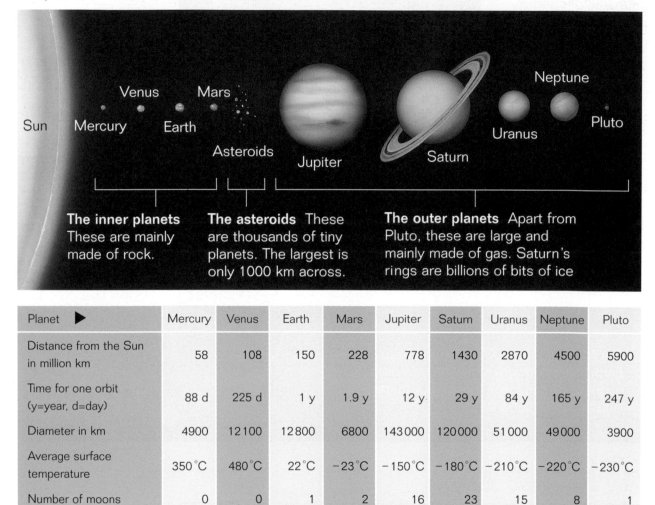

The inner planets These are mainly made of rock.

The asteroids These are thousands of tiny planets. The largest is only 1000 km across.

The outer planets Apart from Pluto, these are large and mainly made of gas. Saturn's rings are billions of bits of ice

Planet ▶	Mercury	Venus	Earth	Mars	Jupiter	Saturn	Uranus	Neptune	Pluto
Distance from the Sun in million km	58	108	150	228	778	1430	2870	4500	5900
Time for one orbit (y=year, d=day)	88 d	225 d	1 y	1.9 y	12 y	29 y	84 y	165 y	247 y
Diameter in km	4900	12100	12800	6800	143000	120000	51000	49000	3900
Average surface temperature	350 °C	480 °C	22 °C	−23 °C	−150 °C	−180 °C	−210 °C	−220 °C	−230 °C
Number of moons	0	0	1	2	16	23	15	8	1

stars

From Earth, a planet looks like a tiny dot in the night sky. Without a telescope, it is difficult to tell whether you are looking at a star or a planet.

planet

We can see planets because they reflect the Sun's light. They are not hot enough to give off their own light.

Orbits

This diagram shows how the sizes of the planets' orbits compare:

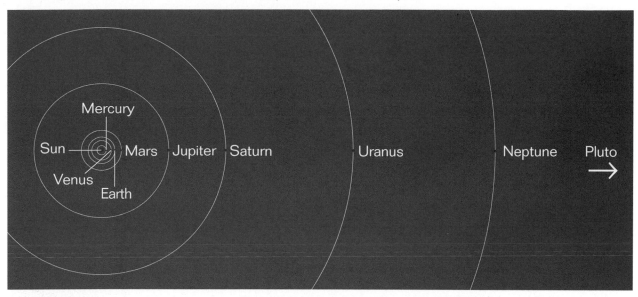

Gravity in action

Gravity is a force.

The Earth's gravity holds us on the ground.

Earth

The Earth's gravity holds the Moon in its orbit around the Earth.

The Sun's gravity holds the Earth and other planets in their orbits around the Sun.

There is a pull of gravity between *all* masses. But to produce a strong pull, one mass has to be very large - like the Earth.

1 Copy and complete each of these sentences by writing in the name of a planet:

The biggest planet is.....
The planet nearest the Sun is.....
The hottest planet is.....
The planet furthest from the Sun is.....
The coldest planet is.....
The planet with most moons is.....
The planet which takes the least time to orbit the Sun is.....
The planet which takes the most time to orbit the Sun is.....

2 Write down the name of the force which holds the planets in their orbits around the Sun.

4.33 Stars and galaxies

The Sun is a star. Other stars look like tiny dots because they are much further away. There are billions of stars. The nearest (apart from the Sun) is *Proxima Centauri*.

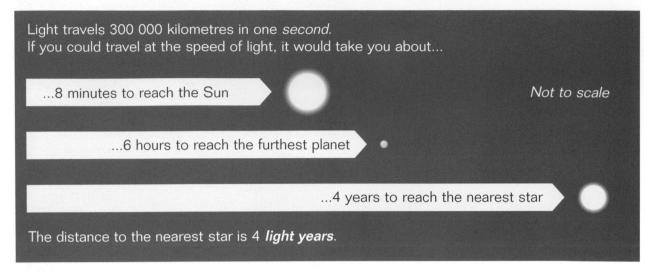

Light travels 300 000 kilometres in one *second*.
If you could travel at the speed of light, it would take you about...

...8 minutes to reach the Sun

Not to scale

...6 hours to reach the furthest planet

...4 years to reach the nearest star

The distance to the nearest star is 4 **light years**.

▶ Galaxies

Our Sun belongs to a huge group of stars called a **galaxy**. This has over 100 billion stars in it. Here is a side-on view:

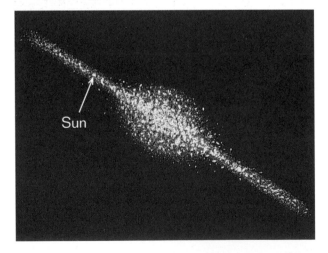

Sun

Our galaxy is called the **Milky Way**. It is so big that a beam of light would take 100 000 years to cross it.

The Andromeda Galaxy is a neighbour of our own galaxy. Its light has taken 2 million years to reach us. It is 2 million light years away.

▶ The Universe

The whole of space is called the **Universe**. Scientists think that there are at least 100 billion galaxies in the Universe.

Birth of a star

A star is formed in a huge cloud of gas and dust called a *nebula*.

This is how the Sun formed, more than 4500 million years ago.

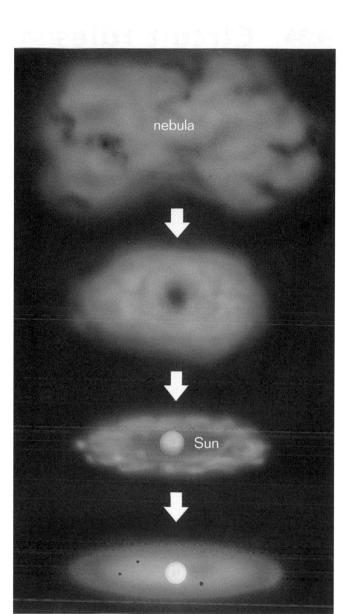

nebula

Sun

Gravity pulled more and more material into a big blob. As bits of material crashed together, they heated up.

When the blob was hot enough, nuclear reactions began - the Sun started to shine.

Around the Sun, smaller blobs of matter cooled to form planets and moons.

1 Choose the word on the right which goes with each of these:
  a The Sun is one example.
  b A huge cloud of gas and dust.
  c A huge group of stars.
  d The whole of space and everything in it.

2 On this spread, find the answers to these questions:
  a How many years does it take light to reach us from the nearest star?
  b How many years does it take light to cross our galaxy?
  c How many years does it take light to reach us from the Andromeda Galaxy?
  d How many stars are there in our galaxy?

Universe

nebula

galaxy

planet

star

4.34 Circuit rules

▶ Finding the resistance

If a conductor has **resistance**, a voltage is needed to make a current flow it. Resistance is measured in **ohms** (Ω). You can calculate it like this:

$$\text{resistance} = \frac{\text{voltage}}{\text{current}}$$

resistance in Ω   voltage in V   current in A

With the circuit on the right, you can measure the resistance of a nichrome coil. The voltage across the coil is changed using the variable resistor. Here are some typical results:

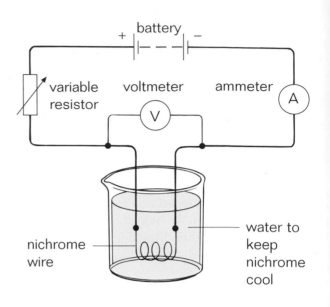

Voltage in V	Current in A	Resistance = $\dfrac{\text{voltage}}{\text{current}}$ in Ω
3.0	1.0	3.0
6.0	2.0	3.0
9.0	3.0	3.0
12.0	4.0	3.0

The resistance stays the same, provided the temperature of the wire doesn't change. This is called **Ohm's law**. It is true for all metal conductors.

▶ Useful equations

The resistance equation can been written using letter symbols and also rearranged:

$$R = \frac{V}{I} \qquad I = \frac{V}{R} \qquad V = I \times R$$

R = resistance   V = voltage   I = current

For example, to find the voltage across a 3 Ω resistor when a current of 2 A flows through, use: $V = I \times R = 2 \times 3 = 6$ V

▶ Working out the power

When a current flows through a resistor, energy is spent and given off as heat. The energy spent per second is called the power (see Spread 4.37). It is measured in watts (W). You can calculate it like this:

$$\begin{array}{ccc} \text{power} & = & \text{voltage} \times \text{current} \\ \text{in W} & & \text{in V} \qquad \text{in A} \end{array}$$

For example, if a resistor has 12 V across it and a current of 2 A through it:

power = voltage x current = 12 x 2 = 24 W

▶ Diode

A **diode** has a very low resistance in one direction, but a very high resistance in the other. So it conducts current in one direction but blocks it in the other.

diode   symbol

▶ Resistors in series

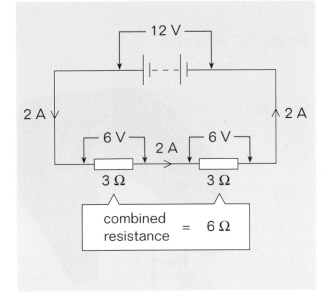

▶ Resistors in parallel

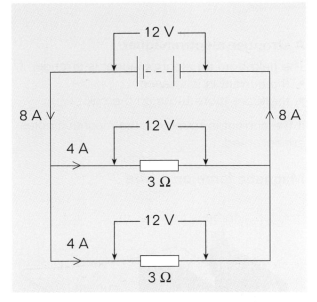

In a circuit like this:
- To find the *combined* resistance, you add the resistances together.
- Each resistor has the same current through it (because the same electrons flow through each).
- The voltages across the resistors add up to equal the battery voltage (because the resistors share the energy from the battery).

In a circuit like this:
- Each resistor gets the full battery voltage.
- The currents through the two resistors add up to equal the current from the battery (because the resistors share the current from the battery).

Current arrows are shown going from the + terminal of the battery round to the −. This is called the **conventional direction**. It is the direction you would expect positive charge to move. Electrons have negative charge, so they actually flow the other way.

1

Work out:
a the resistance of the resistor above.
b the power output from the resistor.

2 If the voltage across a 4 Ω resistor is 8 V, what is the current through it?

3 If a current of 4 A flows through a 6 Ω resistor, what is the voltage across it?

4 Copy the circuit on the right. Write in the readings on the blank meters.

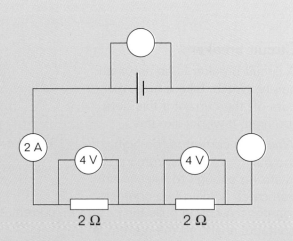

4.35 More electromagnetic effects

▶ A stronger electromagnet

The field from an electromagnet is stronger if
• the current is increased
• there are more turns on the coil.

If the current is reversed, the magnetic poles are reversed.

▶ Magnetic force on a wire

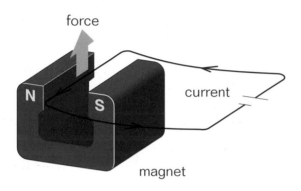

The wire is carrying a current in a magnetic field. The field cause a force on the wire. The force is at *right-angles* to the field.

The force is stronger if
• the current is increased
• a stronger magnet is used.

The direction of the force is reversed if *either* the current is reversed *or* the magnetic field is reversed.

▶ Simple DC motor

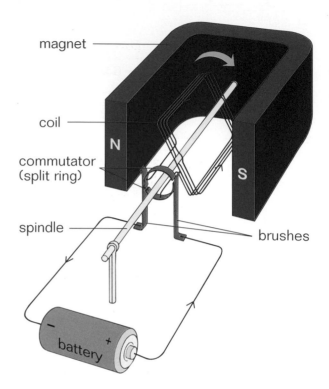

With a current through it, the coil becomes an electromagnet which turns toward the poles of the magnet. Every half turn, the **commutator** reverses the current. So the coil does another half-turn.... and so on.

▶ Circuit breaker

A circuit breaker is an automatic safety switch. Like a fuse, it cuts off the current if this gets too high. It works like this:

When the current is too high, the pull from an electromagnet is strong enough to release an iron catch holding two contacts together. A spring pulls the contacts apart, so the current is switched off.

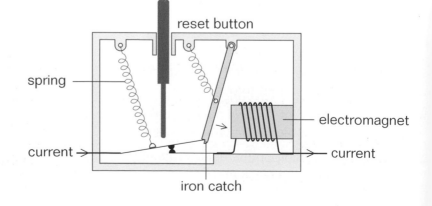

► Loudspeaker

This has a cone which makes the air in front of it vibrate. When these vibrations reach your ears, you hear them as sound.

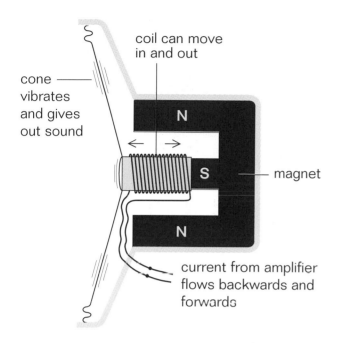

coil can move in and out

cone vibrates and gives out sound

N

S — magnet

N

current from amplifier flows backwards and forwards

An *amplifier* makes current flow backwards and forwards through the coil. The coil pushes and pulls on the magnet. This makes the coil move in and out, so the cone vibrates.

► Transformer

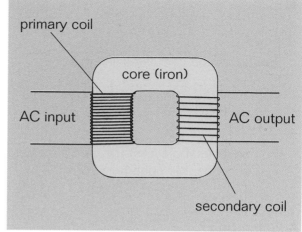

primary coil

core (iron)

AC input

AC output

secondary coil

A transformer can change the voltage of an alternating current. AC in the primary coil produces a changing magnetic field in the core. This generates AC in the secondary coil.

Step-down transformer This *lowers* the voltage. Its secondary coil has *less* turns than its primary.

Step-up transformer This *raises* the voltage. Its secondary coil has *more* turns than its primary.

A transformer cannot give out more power than is put in. If it *raises* the voltage, it *lowers* the current.

1

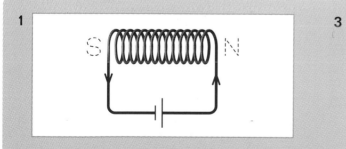

The coil above produces a magnetic field.
a Give *three* ways of making the field stronger.
b How could you reverse the direction of the field?

2 What is each of the following used for?
a Circuit breaker
b Step-up transformer.

3

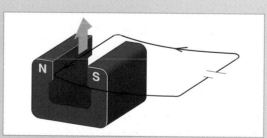

In the experiment above, what would be the effect of doing each of these?
a Increasing the current
b Changing the current direction.

4 Look at the circuit breaker on the opposite page. Explain why the contacts open if the current gets too high.

4.36 More motion and forces

Speed....

Speed can be calculated like this:

$$\text{speed} = \frac{\text{distance travelled}}{\text{time taken}}$$

For example, if a cyclist travels 30 metres in 2 seconds, her speed = 30/2 = 15 m/s.

....and velocity

Velocity is speed in a particular direction.

The direction can be shown with an arrow, like this:

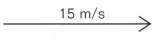

15 m/s

▶ Acceleration

This car below is accelerating. It is gaining velocity:

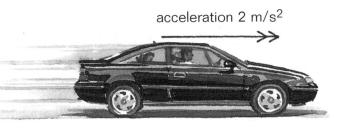

acceleration 2 m/s²

Time	Velocity
0 s	0 m/s
1 s	2 m/s
2 s	4 m/s
3 s	6 m/s
4 s	8 m/s

The car's velocity is going up by 2 metres per second *every second*. The **acceleration** is 2 metres per second², written 2 m/s².

You can calculate acceleration like this:

$$\text{acceleration} = \frac{\text{change in velocity}}{\text{time taken}}$$

For example, as the car's velocity goes up by 8 m/s in 4 s: acceleration = 8/4 = 2 m/s².

▶ Moments

The turning effect of a force is called its **moment**. You calculate it like this:

$$\text{moment} = \text{force} \times \text{distance*}$$
from turning point

(* Shortest distance to the line of the force.)

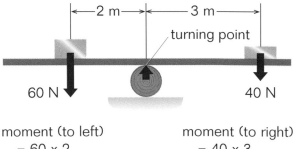

moment (to left)
= 60 x 2
= 120 N m

moment (to right)
= 40 x 3
= 120 N m

This plank balances because the moments to the left and right are equal.

▶ Pressure

You can calculate pressure like this:

$$\text{pressure} = \frac{\text{force}}{\text{area}}$$

For example, if a force of 2000 newtons acts on an area of 2 m², the pressure = 2000/2 = 1000 N/m², also called 2000 **pascal (Pa)**.

Stretching

Below, you can see the effect of a stretching force on a steel wire. As the force increases, so does the **extension** (the length by which the wire stretches). A steel spring also gives a graph of a similar shape.

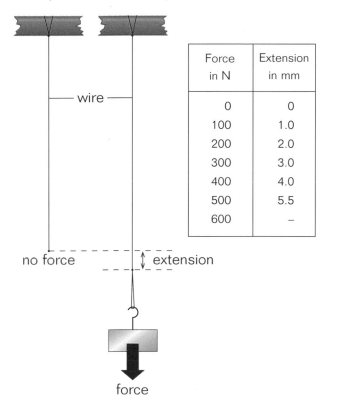

Force in N	Extension in mm
0	0
100	1.0
200	2.0
300	3.0
400	4.0
500	5.5
600	–

no force ⇕ extension

force

Up to point X, each extra 100 newtons of force produces the same extra extension (1 mm in this case). Scientists say that the extension is *proportional to* the stretching force. They call this **Hooke's law**.

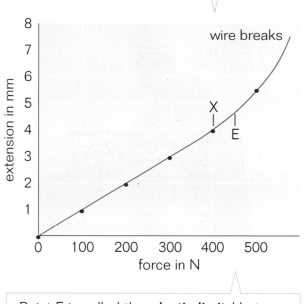

Point E is called the **elastic limit**. Up to here, the wire will return to its original length if the force is removed. Scientists say that the material is **elastic**. Beyond E, the wire becomes permanently stretched.

1 If a cyclist travels 20 metres in 5 seconds, what is her speed?

2 If a cyclist gains 6 m/s of velocity in 3 seconds, what is her acceleration?

3 Below, what weight W (in newtons) is needed to keep the plank balanced?

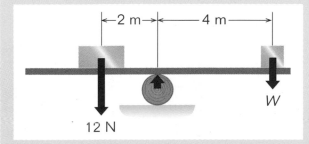

4 If a force of 800 newtons acts on an area of 4 m^2, what is the pressure?

5 When a spring was stretched, these readings were taken:

Force in N	0	1	2	3	4	5
Length in mm	40	49	58	67	79	99

a Make a table and draw a graph of *extension* against *force*.
b On your graph, mark the point where the spring stops obeying Hooke's Law.
c What force produces an extension of 21 mm?

EXTENSION

4.37 Work, energy, and power

▶ Work

If a force makes something move, scientists say that **work** is done.

Like energy, work is measured in **joules (J)**:

1 joule of work is done when... a force of 1 newton (N)...

...moves a distance of 1 metre (m)

You can calculate work like this:

work done = force x distance moved*
in J   in N   in m

(* in the direction of the force.)

For example, if a force of 3 N moves a distance of 2 m: work done = 3 x 2 = 6 J.

▶ Linking work and energy

There is a link between work and energy. If, say, 50 joules of work are done, then 50 joules of energy are spent:

50 J of energy spent ▶ 50 J of work done ▶ 50 J of energy gained

▶ Power

If one engine has more **power** than another, it can do work at a faster rate.

Power is measured in **watts (W)**.

A power of 1 watt means that work is being done at the rate of 1 joule per second. So energy is being spent at the rate of 1 joule per second.

You can calculate power like this:

$$power = \frac{work\ done}{time\ taken}$$

$$or \quad power = \frac{energy\ spent}{time\ taken}$$

For example, if a motor does 300 J of work in 3 seconds: power = 300/3 = 100 W

Larger units of power

1 **kilowatt (kW)** = 1000 watts

1 **megawatt (MW)** = 1 000 000 watts ('mega' means 'million')

Typical powers

human engine 400 W

washing machine motor 250 W

small car engine 45 000 W (45 kW)

Land Rover engine 70 000 W (70 kW)

Efficiency

When fuels burn, much of their energy is wasted as heat. In a power station for example, for every 100 joules of energy in the fuel, only 35 joules ends up as electrical energy. The *efficiency* is 35%.

Here are some typical efficiency values:

For every **100 J** of **Input energy** ▶		Output energy	Efficiency
petrol engine		25 J	25 %
diesel engine		35 J	35 %
fuel-burning power station		35 J	35 %
human body		15 J	15 %

Low efficiency is not because of poor design. When an engine is working, it impossible to stop some energy being wasted as heat.

Paying for electricity

You have to pay for electrical energy from the mains. A meter measures the energy in units called *kilowatt hours (kW h)*.

1 kW h is the energy supplied if a 1 kW appliance is switched on for 1 hour.
(1 kW h = 3 600 000 joules)

You can calculate energy supplied, like this:

$$\text{energy in kW h} = \text{power in kW} \times \text{time taken in hours}$$

This is how you calculate the cost:

Using a 3 kW heater for 4 hours

Energy = power × time
= 3 KW × 4 h
= 12 kW h

The Electricity Board charges 10p per kW h (unit). So,

cost = 12 × 10p
= 120p
= £1.20

---

1 If a 20 N force moves something 5 metres, how much work is done?

2 If you do 100 joules of work in 10 seconds, what is your power output?

3 If electrical energy cost 10p per kW h:
   a How much energy (in kW h) is needed to run a 2 kW fan heater for 4 hours?
   b What is the cost of running the fan heater for 4 hours?
   c On the right, what is the cost of the electricity supplied in 24 hours?

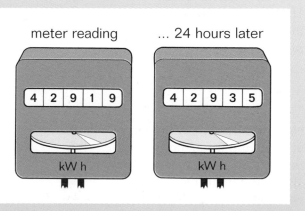

meter reading   ... 24 hours later

4 2 9 1 9   4 2 9 3 5

kW h   kW h

4.38 Waves and rays

▶ Longitudinal and transverse waves

Waves carry energy. They can travel through many materials. Here are two types of waves that can travel through a stretched spring:

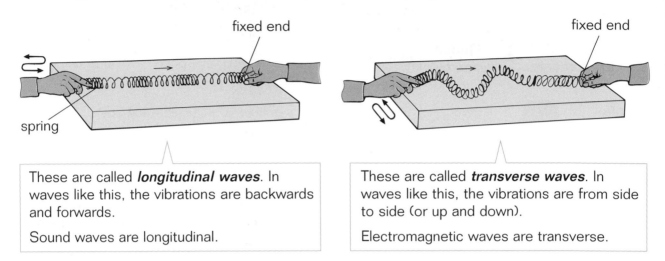

fixed end   fixed end

spring

These are called **longitudinal waves**. In waves like this, the vibrations are backwards and forwards.

Sound waves are longitudinal.

These are called **transverse waves**. In waves like this, the vibrations are from side to side (or up and down).

Electromagnetic waves are transverse.

▶ Frequency

The number of waves sent out per second is called the **frequency** (see also Spread 4.21).

Frequency is measured in **hertz**:

1 hertz (Hz)	means 1 wave per second
1 kilohertz (kHz)	means 1000 waves per second
1 megahertz (MHz)	means 1 000 000 waves per second

▶ Wavelength and amplitude

A vibrating dipper is sending waves across the surface of some water. The diagram shows what the terms **wavelength** and **amplitude** mean.

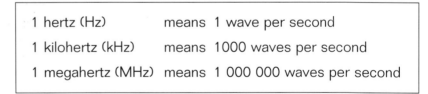

wavelength

amplitude

wavelength

Now, the dipper is vibrating at *twice* the frequency. As a result, the wave peaks are closer together: the wavelength is *half* what is was before.

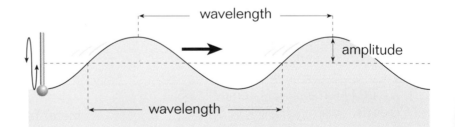

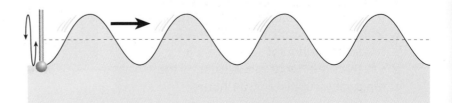

Sounds on screen

Sound waves are longitudinal. But when they are displayed on an oscilloscope, the line goes up and down (see Spread 4.20).

Here are four different sounds, as seen on an oscilloscope:

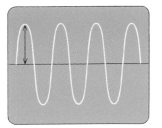 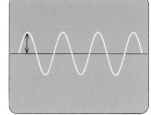

This sound is louder...   ...than this.

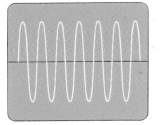 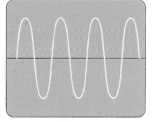

This sound has a higher pitch...   ...than this.

Radiation

The things below all radiate (spread out) from their source, so they are types of radiation:

Sound waves	Electromagnetic radiation: radio waves microwaves infrared light
Alpha particles	ultraviolet X-rays
Beta particles	gamma rays

-------- **Ionizing radiation** --------

Some radiations are ionizing: they have enough energy to turn atoms in their path into ions (see Spread 3.23). Ionization is harmful because it can kill or damage living cells, or make them grow abnormally as cancers.

Background radiation This is very weak, ionizing radiation which is around us all the time. It comes from space, and from radioactive materials in the ground and air.

---

1 The diagram on the right shows some waves moving across water, actual size.

  Use a ruler marked in mm to measure
  a the wavelength of the waves.
  b the amplitude of the waves.

2 A loudspeaker gives out 5000 sound waves per second. What is its frequency in kHz?

3 A VHF radio station broadcasts on a frequency of 100 MHz. How many radio waves does it send out every second?

4 Why are ionizing radiations harmful?

5 Look at the radiations listed on the right.
  a Which ones are ionizing?
  b Which ones are electromagnetic?

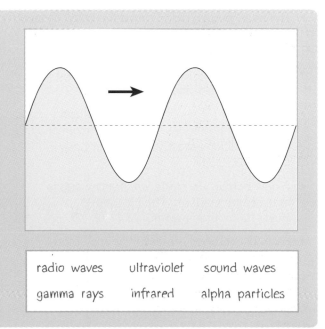

| radio waves | ultraviolet | sound waves |
| gamma rays | infrared | alpha particles |

Key ideas

The spread numbers in brackets tell you where to find more information.

Features of life

- Living things need food and air. They reproduce, react, make waste, grow, and move. *(2.1)*

- Living things are made from cells. *(2.1, 2.28)*

- In cells, energy is released from food. This is called respiration. *(2.2, 2.28)*

- Unlike animal cells, plants cells have a tough cell wall, and chlorophyll for absorbing the energy in sunlight. *(2.1, 2.28)*

- Cells can grow, split to form new cells... and so on, until a whole body is made. *(2.21)*

The human body

- Your body has lots of organs. Each one has a special job to do. *(2.6)*

- Your skeleton gives you support, protects organs, and lets you move. Joints are moved by muscles attached to the skeleton. *(2.7)*

- Food is a mixture of carbohydrates, fats, proteins, fibre, minerals, vitamins, and water. For a balanced diet, you need the right amounts of all of these. *(2.15, 2.31)*

- In your gut, food is digested so that useful things can get into your blood. *(2.8, 2.31)*

- The heart pumps blood round the body. Blood delivers food, water, and oxygen to cells and carries away their waste. *(2.6, 2.9)*

- In the lungs, oxygen gets into your blood and carbon dioxide comes out. *(2.10)*

- Your different organs are controlled using nerves and hormones. Together, they must keep conditions steady inside your body. *(2.7, 2.13, 2.31)*

- A new human life starts when a tiny egg is fertilized by a sperm. The baby develops inside its mother's womb. *(2.11, 2.12)*

- Harmful microbes are called germs. If they get into your body, they cause disease. *(2.16)*

- For healthy living, you should eat sensibly and take exercise. Smoking, alcohol, drugs, and solvents can all damage your health. *(2.17)*

Plants

- In their leaves, plants make food and oxygen from carbon dioxide and water. This is called photosynthesis. To do it, plants need the energy in sunlight. *(2.2, 2.3, 2.28)*

- Plants have a system of tubes for carrying water and minerals from their roots to their leaves. Other tubes carry food from the leaves to storage areas. *(2.2, 2.3, 2.28)*

- Plant growth is controlled by hormones. *(2.3)*

- To make a seed, a male cell from a pollen grain must join with a female cell in a flower's ovary. Pollen grains are carried to other flowers by insects or the wind. *(2.4, 2.5)*

- To start growing into a new plant, a seed needs water, warmth, and air. *(2.5)*

The variety of life

- Scientists put living things into groups by looking for features that are similar. *(2.18. 2.19)*

- In any one species (type of animal or plant), individuals vary. *(2.20)*

- Animals and plants inherit many of their features from their parents. Genes store the inherited information. They are in chromosomes in cells. *(2.21, 2.29)*

- Fossils give scientists clues about how life has evolved on Earth. *(2.30)*.

Living together

- Animals and plants have features which make them adapted (suited) to their habitat and way of life. *(2.23, 2.30)*

- Animals get their energy by eating plants or other animals. Every plant and animal is part of a food chain. *(2.24, 2.31)*

- Some microbes feed on dead plants and animals. They help in the recycling of carbon and other substances. *(2.26)*

- Humans are causing pollution and disturbing the atmosphere. *(2.22, 2.27)*

Key ideas

The spread numbers in brackets tell you where to find more information.

Features of materials

- Substances can be solid, liquid, or gas. *(3.1, 3.2, 3.8)*

- Everything is made from about 90 simple substances called elements. An atom is the smallest bit of an element. *(3.4)*

- With many substances, the smallest bit is a group of atoms called a molecule. *(3.4, 3.23)*

- Atoms have a nucleus of protons and neutrons, with electrons moving around it. *(3.8)*

- How an element behaves chemically depends on how its electrons are arranged. *(3.23)*

- There are two main types of element: metals and nonmetals. *(3.4, 3.24)*

- Most metals are shiny, solid, and good conductors of heat and electricity. Most nonmetals are insulators. *(3.3, 3.4, 4.1, 4.15)*

- Elements can join together to form new substances, called compounds. *(3.4)*

- Mixtures are made up of different substances which have not joined chemically. *(3.5, 3.6)*

- Air is a mixture of gases. *(3.16)*

Looking for patterns

- The periodic table is a chart of all the elements. Elements in the same group have similar properties. *(3.24)*

- The reactivity series is a list of metals. arranged in order of reactivity. *(3.25)*

- Some chemicals reactions are reversible. *(3.26)*

- The rate of a reaction depends on the size of the bits, concentration, temperature, and whether a catalyst is being used. *(3.26)*

- If an acid reacts with a metal, hydrogen gas is given off. *(3.7, 3.11)*

- If an acid reacts with a carbonate, carbon dioxide gas is given out. *(3.11)*

- An alkali can neutralize an acid (cancel out its acid effect). If an alkali neutralizes an acid, a salt is made. *(3.7, 3.25)*

Changing materials

- The signs of a chemical change are: new substance(s) made; change difficult to reverse; energy given out or taken out. *(3.9)*

- Burning is a chemical change. So is corrosion. *(3.10, 3.12)*

- When an element combines with oxygen (as in burning), an oxide is produced. *(3.25)*

- Most materials expand when heated. Expansion is an example of a physical change. *(3.2, 3.9)*

- Oil was produced by chemical changes. It formed from the remains of plants and animals which lived millions of years ago. *(3.15, 4.18)*

- Oil a mixture of hydrocarbons. It contains fuels such as petrol and diesel oil. *(3.15)*

- When hydrocarbons burn, the products are carbon dioxide and water. *(3.10)*

- Substances in oil can be used to make new materials, such as plastics. *(3.15)*

- We get our metals from the ground. Most are in compounds called ores. *(3.12, 3.13)*

- Limestone is used to make cement and concrete. It is also needed for steelmaking. *(3.14)*

- Nitrogen, from the air, is used to make ammonia. Ammonia is used to make nitric acid and fertilizers. *(3.17)*

- Since the Earth was formed, the mixture of gases in its atmosphere has changed. *(3.27)*

- The three main types of rock are: igneous, sedimentary, and metamorphic *(3.20, 3.27)*

- In time, the surface of rocks becomes weathered, then eroded (worn away). *(3.19)*

- Bits of rock may be moved, buried, and crushed to form new rock. In this way, rock is recycled. *(3.19, 3.27)*

- The Earth's outer layer is made up of huge sections called plates. These move very slowly. Their movements cause earthquakes, volcanoes, and mountain-building. *(3.21, 3.22)*

Key ideas

The spread numbers in brackets tell you where to find more information.

Electricity and magnetism
- There are two types of charge (+ and −). Like charges repel; unlike charges attract. *(4.1)*
- A current is a flow of electrons. *(4.2)*
- The higher the voltage of a battery, the more energy each electron has to spend. *(4.2)*
- A higher voltage causes a higher current. *(4.3, 4.34)*
- When a current flows through a resistance, energy is given off as heat. *(4.4, 4.34)*
- Bulbs and resistors can be connected in series or in parallel. *(4.3, 4.34)*
- A magnet has two poles (N and S). Like poles repel; unlike poles attract. *(4.5)*
- An electromagnet produces a magnetic field when a current flows through it. *(4.5, 4.35)*
- There is a force on a current in a magnetic field. Electric motors use this effect. *(4.35)*
- A current can be generated by moving a magnet near a coil, or a coil near a magnet. Generators use this effect. *(4.6)*
- Mains electricity is AC (alternating current). It comes from power stations. *(4.6, 4.7)*
- Transformers change AC voltages. *(4.6, 4.35)*
- There are equations for calculating resistance and power. *(4.34, 4.37, page 211)*

Forces and motion
- If something is staying still, or moving at a steady speed in a straight line, the forces on it are balanced. *(4.8)*
- If a force is concentrated on a small area, the pressure is high. *(4.9, 4.36)*
- Liquids transmit pressure. *(4.10)*
- A force has a stronger turning effect if it is moved further away from a pivot. *(4.11, 4.36)*
- Forces can make things stretch. *(4.36)*
- There are equations for calculating speed, acceleration, moment of a force, and pressure. *(4.36, page 211)*

Waves and rays
- Light travels much faster than sound. *(4.20)*
- Light and sound can be reflected. *(4.22, 4.23, 4.25)*
- Some materials refract (bend) light. *(4.24)*
- A prism will split white light into a range of colours called a spectrum. *(4.27)*
- Depending on the sound waves, sounds can be high or low, loud or quiet. *(4.21, 4.38)*
- Light is one member of a whole family of electromagnetic waves. *(4.28, 4.38)*

The Earth and beyond
- As the Earth turns, we get day and night. *(4.30)*
- The Moon orbits the Earth. The Earth and other planets orbit the Sun. Gravitational forces keep them in orbit. *(4.31, 4.32)*
- Satellites can pass on signals, watch the weather, and carry telescopes. *(4.31)*
- The Sun is one star in a galaxy of over 100 billion stars. *(4.33)*

Energy
- Nearly all the world's energy comes from the Sun. *(4.18, 4.19)*
- Some power stations use coal, oil, natural gas, or nuclear fuel. Others use renewable energy sources. *(4.17, 4.18, 4.19)*
- Energy can change into different forms, but it can't be made or destroyed. *(4.13, 4.14)*
- Heat can be transferred by conduction, convection, and radiation. *(4.15, 4.16)*
- There are equations linking force, work, energy, and power. *(4.37, page 211)*

Radioactivity
- Radioactive materials give off nuclear radiation. *(4.29, 4.38)*
- Nuclear radiation is harmful. But it weakens in time. *(4.29, 4.38)*

Words and meanings

The spread numbers in brackets tell you where to find more information.

acceleration If something has an acceleration of 10 m/s^2, its speed is increasing by 10 m/s every second. *(4.36)*

acids These substances turn blue litmus red. They attack carbonates and some metals. They all contain hydrogen. *(3.7, 3.25)*

alkalis These substances turn red litmus blue. They can neutralize acids (cancel out their acid effect). *(3.7, 3.25)*

alloy A mixture of a metal and other substances (often metals). *(3.5)*

atom The smallest bit of an element. It is made of protons, neutrons, and electrons. *(3.8, 3.23).*

cells *(living)* Tiny units from which animals and plants are made. There are millions of cells in your body. *(2.1, 2.28)*

chromosomes Thread-like bits in the nucleus of a cell. They are chains of genes. *(2.21, 2.29)*

compound New substance formed when two or more chemical elements combine. *(3.4)*

condense Change from a gas to a liquid. *(3.2)*

conductor A material which lets an electric current pass through easily. Or a material which lets heat pass through easily. *(3.3, 4.1, 4.15)*

current This is measured in amperes (A). It is a flow of electric charge. The charge is usually billions of tiny electrons. *(4.2, 4.3, 4.34)*

density If a material with a mass of 1000 kg has a volume of 1 cubic metre, then its density is 1000 kg/m^3. *(3.1)*

diffusion One material spreading through another because its atoms or molecules are moving about. *(3.8)*

digestion Turning food into a liquid that can be taken into the blood. *(2.8, 2.31)*

element *(chemical)* Substance containing only one type of atom. There are about 100 different elements and everything is made from them. *(3.4, 3.23, 3.24)*

enzyme Natural chemical that speeds up vital reactions inside the body. *(2.8, 2.31, 3.26)*

erosion The wearing away of rocks and soil. *(3.19, 3.27)*

evaporate Change from a liquid to a gas. *(3.2, 4.16)*

force A push or pull. It is measured in newtons (N). *(4.8, 4.36)*

fossil fuels Fuels formed from the remains of ancient plants and animals. Oil, natural gas, and coil are the main ones. *(2.26, 4.18, 4.19)*

frequency If 100 sound waves are sent out every second, then the frequency of the sound is 100 hertz (Hz). *(4.21, 4.38)*

galaxy Huge group of stars. Our Sun is one star in a galaxy of over 100 billion stars. *(4.33)*

gene A section of a chromosome (in a cell). It carries information about one inherited feature. *(2.21, 2.29)*

habitat The place where an animal or plant lives. *(2.22)*

hormones Chemicals, made in the bodies of animals and plants, which control how different organs work. *(2.3, 2.13)*

insulator A material which does not let an electric current pass through. Or a material which lets very little heat pass through. *(3.3, 4.1, 4.15)*

ions Atoms that have gained or lost electrons, so are negatively (−) or positively (+) charged. *(3.23)*

isotopes Different versions of atoms of the same element. Their atoms have the same number of protons and electrons, but different numbers of neutrons. *(3.23)*

mass The amount of matter in something. It is measured in kilograms (kg). *(3.1)*

microbes Microscopic living things. Bacteria and viruses are examples. *(2.16, 2.25, 2.26)*

mineral Any useful substance that can be got from the ground. *(2.2)*

molecule A group of atoms stuck together so that they act like a single particle. *(3.4, 3.23)*

nucleus *(of atom)* The centre part, made from protons and (usually) neutrons. *(3.8, 3.23)*

nucleus *(of cell)* The part which controls the cell and stores the inherited information. *(2.1, 2.28)*

organ Part of the body of an animal or plant with a particular job to do. The heart, lungs, liver, and eyes are all organs. *(2.6, 2.28)*

ovary Organ that produces the female sex cells in an animal or flower. *(2.3, 2.11)*

ovum Egg (female sex cell) of a woman (or female animal). *(2.11, 2.21, 2.29)*

photosynthesis Food-making that happen in the leaves of plants. The energy in sunlight is used to turn carbon dioxide and water into glucose sugar. *(2.2, 2.28)*

poles Points near the end of a magnet where the magnetic forces seem to come from. *(4.5)*

power If something is spending energy at the rate of 100 joules every second, then its power is 100 watts (W). *(4.4, 4.37)*

pressure If a force of 1 newton pushes on an area of 1 square metre, then the pressure is 1 N/m^2, also called 1 pascal (Pa). *(4.9, 4.10, 4.36)*

products Substances made in a chemical reaction. *(3.11)*

proteins Substances made in cells and needed to build the bodies of living things. *(2.15)*

radiation Any waves or tiny particles that radiate (spread out) from their source. Light, microwaves, X-rays, and sound are examples. *(4.16, 4.28, 4.29, 4.38)*

radioactive A radioactive material contains unstable atoms which give out nuclear radiation. *(4.29)*

reaction *(chemical)* A change in which atoms join together in a different way to form new substances. *(3.9, 3.11, 3.25, 3.26)*

refraction The bending of light as it passes in or out of a material such as glass or water. *(4.24, 4.27)*

resistance This is measured in ohms (Ω). If a material has a high resistance, it does not conduct an electric current easily. *(4.4, 4.34)*

respiration Releasing energy from food. It happens in the cells of living things and usually uses up oxygen. *(2.2, 2.28, 3.10)*

Solar System The Sun and its planets. *(4.32)*

solution Mixture in which one substance has dissolved in another. *(3.5)*

solvent A liquid used to dissolve something. For example, water is a solvent for salt. *(3.5, 3.8)*

species One type of animal or plant. *(2.30)*

speed If something travels 5 metres every second, its speed is 5 m/s. *(4.12, 4.36)*

sperm Sex cell of a man (or male animal). *(2.11, 2.21, 2.29)*

strata Layers of rock. *(3.21)*

transformer Equipment used to change the voltage of an alternating current. *(4.6, 4.35)*

ultrasound Sound too high for the human ear to hear, with a frequency above 20 000 Hz. *(4.22)*

Universe The whole of space and everything in it. *(4.33)*

uterus The womb, where a new baby develops. *(2.11, 2.12)*

vertebrates Animals with backbones. Mammals, birds, and fish are examples. *(2.19)*

voltage This is measured in volts (V). The higher the voltage of a battery, the more energy it gives to each bit of charge it pushes out. *(4.2, 4.3, 4.34)*

wavelength The distance from one wave 'peak' to the next. *(4.28, 4.38)*

weight The downward force of gravity on something. *(4.8, 4.11)*

work If a force of 1 newton moves something a distance of 1 metre, then 1 joule of work is done. *(4.37)*

Useful equations

The spread number in brackets tells you where to find more information.

$$\text{density} = \frac{\text{mass}}{\text{volume}} \quad (3.1)$$

$$\text{moment} = \text{force} \times \text{distance from turning point} \quad (4.36)$$

$$\text{resistance} = \frac{\text{voltage}}{\text{current}} \quad (4.34)$$

$$\text{pressure} = \frac{\text{force}}{\text{area}} \quad (4.36)$$

$$\text{power} = \text{voltage} \times \text{current} \quad (4.34)$$

$$\text{work done} = \text{force} \times \text{distance moved} \quad (4.37)$$

$$\text{speed} = \frac{\text{distance travelled}}{\text{time taken}} \quad (4.36)$$

$$\text{power} = \frac{\text{work done}}{\text{time taken}} = \frac{\text{energy spent}}{\text{time taken}} \quad (4.37)$$

$$\text{acceleration} = \frac{\text{change in velocity}}{\text{time taken}} \quad (4.36)$$

$$\text{energy spent} = \text{power} \times \text{time taken} \quad (4.37)$$

GCSE Questions

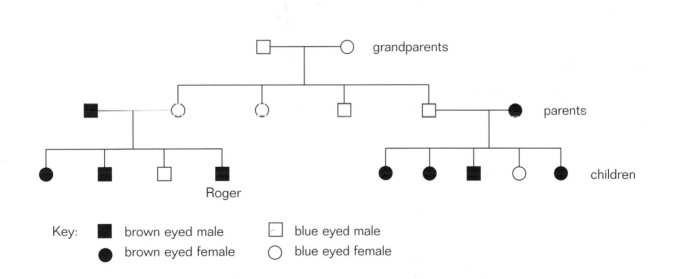

Key:
- ■ brown eyed male
- ● brown eyed female
- ☐ blue eyed male
- ○ blue eyed female

1 The diagram above shows a family tree.

  a How many people in the family tree had brown eyes?

  b How many males had brown eyes?

  c Who has Roger inherited his brown eyes from?

(MEG adapted question)

2 The lifestyle of a person can affect their health.

  a Suggest a way in which each of these actions can damage a person's health.

    i) A diet rich in fat and lacking in fibre.

    ii) Smoking cigarettes.

  b Suggest a way in which regular exercise can improve a person's health.

(EDEXCEL)

3 The drawing shows a pea plant.

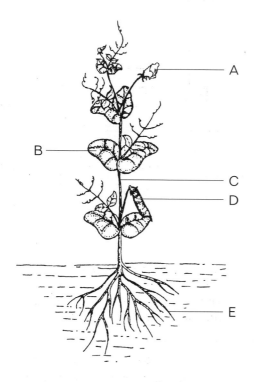

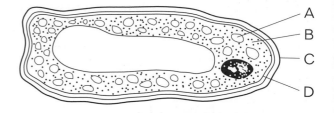

Thrips feed on the stem of the pea plant.

Beetles feed on the pea seeds.

Eelworms feed on the roots.

Bees collect pollen from the stamens.

a Which of the labels, A to E, shows
  i)   where the thrips feed?
  ii) where the beetles feed?
  iii) where the eelworms feed?
  iv) where the bees collect pollen?

b Copy the following and fill in the missing words:
  If pea plants are grown close together, they do not grow very well. This is because they compete with each other for ..... and .....

c The eelworms destroy many of the roots. Give *two* reasons why the pea plants do not grow well when the roots are destroyed.

d Greenflies feed on the leaves of the pea plant. Ladybirds feed on these greenflies.
  i)   Show this information as a food chain.
  ii) Draw a ring round the predator in this food chain.
  iii) Some people think that ladybirds are pests and should be killed. Do you agree with this? Give your reason.

e Mesophyll cells in the leaves of the pea plant make sugars. The diagram above shows a section through a mesophyll cell. Name the structures A, B, C and D.

(NEAB)

4 This key lists organs of the human body:

Letter	Organ
A	Brain
B	Heart
C	Lung
D	Stomach
E	Large intestine
F	Kidney
G	Bladder

The table below shows a function of each of these organs. Copy the table. Match the correct function to each organ by writing the correct letter in each box. The first one has been done for you.

Function	Letter
Stores waste fluid called urine	G
Breaks food down into smaller chemicals	
Pumps blood around the body	
Controls other organs	
Filters the blood to help remove waste	
Helps oxygen to enter the blood and carbon dioxide to leave	
Takes water from food into the blood stream	

(EDEXCEL)

5 Power stations release waste gases into the atmosphere.

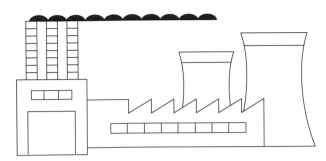

a Burning fossil fuels in power stations makes carbon dioxide. Name two other gases made when fossil fuels burn.

b The release of these gases into the atmosphere may damage the environment. Describe, in as much detail as possible, how this happens.

(NEAB)

6 The diagram shows a cross-section of a type of volcano.

lava flow

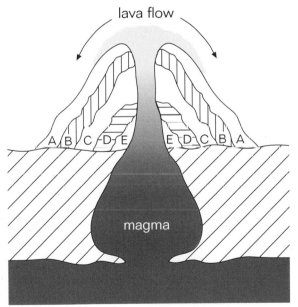

magma

a What type of rocks are produced by volcanoes?

b Which of the labelled layers, A, B, C, D, or E, is the oldest?

c Explain why crystals on the surface of rock layer A are smaller than the crystals in the middle of the same layer.

(MEG)

7 The diagram below shows a camping stove used by some students.

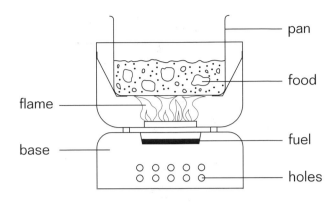

A student wrote the report below to explain how the stove works. The report has had some words removed. Copy and complete the report using words from this list:

air	chemical change	liquids
argon	physical change	nitrogen
gases	carbon dioxide	heat energy
solids	water vapour	oxygen

To use the stove, a fuel called methylated spirits is poured into the burner and lit with a match.

The holes in the base let ..... into the stove. This contains the gas called ..... which is needed for the fuel to burn.

When the fuel burns, new substances are formed. This shows that a ..... takes place.

When all of the methylated spirits has burned, nothing is left in the burner. This shows that the new substances must all be ..... .

Methylated spirits contain carbon and hydrogen. When the fuel burns, the carbon is changed into ..... .

The hydrogen is changed into ..... .

When the fuel burns, it gives out ..... which cooks the food in the pan.

(NEAB)

8 A list of substances is given below.

chalk   chlorine   copper sulphate
fluorine   copper   potassium chloride
sodium   hydrogen   sodium hydroxide
gold   granite

Choose a substance which fits each of the descriptions below. Use only substances from the list. You may use the substances in the list as many times as you wish.

a A metallic element which reacts vigorously with cold water.

b A halogen used to kill germs in drinking water.

c A transition element.

d A compound which forms a coloured solution in water.

e A halogen often present as one of its compounds in toothpaste.

f An alkali.

(EDEXCEL)

9 In each of the diagrams below, different atoms are shown by ○ and ●

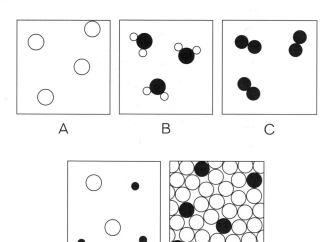

Which of the diagrams could represent

a oxygen gas (O_2)?

b a mixture of solids?

c steam?

d a gas such as helium (He)?

e a gaseous mixture of argon (Ar) and neon (Ne)?

(MEG)

10 This label has been taken from a bottle of *Corona Lemonade*.

a Use the list of ingredients to help you answer this question.
Name a substance in the lemonade which
   i) could be fermented into alcohol.
   ii) will turn blue litmus red.

b The preservative in *Corona Lemonade* is sodium benzoate. Its formula can be represented as:

$$C_6H_5CO_2Na$$

   i) Name the metal present in the compound.
   ii) State the number of different elements present in the compound.

(NEAB)

11 The diagram shows the Earth and the Sun (not drawn to scale).

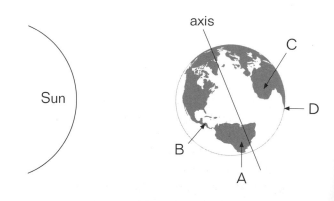

a Which country (A–D) is in daylight?

b Copy and complete the sentences below, using words from this list:

day   month   week   year

The Earth moves round the Sun once each ..... . It takes the Earth one ..... to spin once on its axis.

(NEAB)

12 The diagrams show a hair-dryer and the circuit inside the hair-dryer.

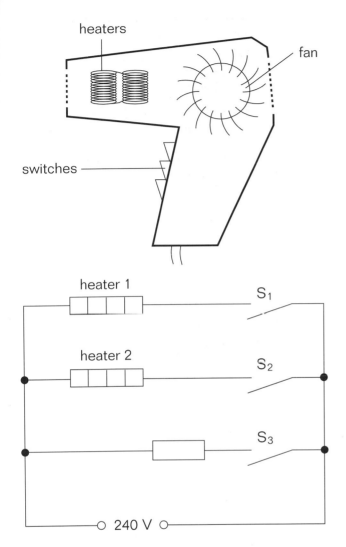

a Switches S_1, S_2 and S_3 are all shown in the OFF position. Which switch or switches have to be ON to make
  i) only the fan work?
  ii) both heaters work?

b i) What happens to the current in the circuit when the heaters are switched on?
  ii) Suggest why it is important to have the fan working when the heaters are switched on.

c This hair-dryer has a plastic case. It is connected to a mains socket by a 3-pin plug. The cable connecting the hair-dryer to the plug contains only two wires.
  i) What are the colours of the insulation on the two wires?

  ii) Which of the usual three wires is not needed?
  iii) This hair-dryer is safe to use without the third wire. Explain why.

d The following information is stamped on the hair-dryer:

Electrical supply	240 V	50 Hz
Maximum power	1300 W	

  i) Which number tells us how fast the hair-dryer uses energy?
  ii) On what else does the energy used by the hair-dryer depend?

(NEAB)

13 This is a list of types of wave:

gamma	*infrared*
light	*microwaves*
radio	*ultraviolet*
X-rays	

Choose from the list the type of wave which best fits each of these descriptions:

a Stimulates the sensitive cells on the retina.

b Necessary for a suntan.

c Used for rapid cooking in an oven.

d Used to take a photograph of the bones in a broken leg.

e Emitted by a television remote control unit.

(MEG)

14 a Coal is a fossil fuel.
  i) Name one other fossil fuel.
  ii) Describe how fossil fuels were formed.
  iii) What is meant by a fuel?
  iv) Name one fuel which is not a fossil fuel.

b Coal is a non-renewable energy resource. Explain what is meant by a non-renewable energy resource.

(NEAB)

15 The drawing shows a tyre used on a large, earth-moving vehicle.

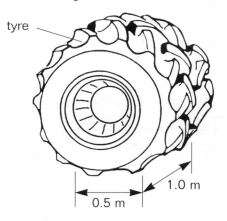

tyre

1.0 m

0.5 m

a When the vehicle is loaded, the area of each tyre in contact with the ground is a rectangle of sides l.0 m by 0.5 m.
  i) Calculate the area of contact of one tyre with the ground.
  ii) The vehicle has four of these tyres. Calculate the total area in contact with the ground.

b When the vehicle is loaded it weighs 100 000 N. Calculate the pressure exerted on the ground by the tyres.

(NEAB)

16 The following table gives information about some of the planets:

Planet	Distance from the Sun (million kilometres)	Diameter (kilometres)	Mass compared to the Earth
Earth	149	13 000	1
Jupiter	773	142 000	320
Mars	227	6 720	0.11
Mercury	58	4 800	0.06
Venus	108	12 000	0.8

Use the information given in the table to answer the following questions:

a On which of these planets is the surface temperature likely to be the lowest?

b Which of the planets orbits closest to the Earth?

c Which is the smallest of these planets?

d Which of these planets is most similar in size to the Earth?

(EDEXCEL)

Answers to questions

2.1
1 plants; cells; body; nucleus **2** a) Cat eating b) Flower dropping seeds c) Dog barking when you move d) Plant growing towards the light **3** nucleus (top left), animal (bottom left), cell wall (top right), plant (bottom right).

2.2
1 Leaves shaded in **2** sunlight; carbon dioxide, oxygen; oxygen, carbon dioxide; oxygen **3** Water goes in through roots, then moves up water tubes **4** Minerals go in through roots with water **5** Gases pass in and out through tiny holes

2.3
1 a) glucose b) starch c) light d) hormone **2** ...they contain chlorophyll; ...the light; ...the Earth; ...it makes roots grow more quickly

2.4
1 pollen (top left), nectar (bottom left), ovules (top right), petal (bottom right) **2** female; male; pollination **3** a) To attract insects b) Looking for nectar c) Pollen sticks to bee's body, bee flies to another flower, pollen sticks to this flower

2.5
1 fertilization; germination **2** Sentence order is 5th, 2nd, 6th, 3rd, 1st, 4th **3** Water, warmth, air **4** Seed falls slowly and is blown by wind

2.6
1 a) stomach b) lung c) heart d) kidney **2** Brain (in head); lung (in chest) **3** Food, water, oxygen **4** From kidneys (through bladder), from lungs

2.7
1 skull; ribs; backbone **2** a) teeth b) muscles c) nerves **3** calcium; ligaments; tendons

2.8
1 blood; digestion; enzymes **2** Sentence order is 3rd, 6th, 1st, 5th, 2nd, 4th

2.9
1 white; red **2** a) artery b) vein **3** Heart is in middle, oxygen is collected in lungs, oxygen is delivered to body

2.10

1 From top: windpipe, lung, heart, rib, diaphragm 2 ribs, diaphragm, lungs, blood 3 Oxygen 4 carbon dioxide 5 You have to 'burn up' food faster, so more oxygen needed

2.11

1 Sentence order is 3rd, 2nd, 1st 2 a) testicles b) ovaries c) fertilization

2.12

1 a) bag of watery liquid b) umbilical cord c) placenta 2 Sentence order is 5th, 4th, 1st, 6th, 3rd, 2nd 3 Baby's blood gets food and oxygen from mother's blood, in the placenta

2.13

1 a) receptors b) nerves c) hormones 2 a) adrenalin b) adrenal glands c) insulin 3 Because their bodies do not make enough insulin to deal with their blood sugar.

2.14

1 Top, from left to right: hair, dead cells, receptor. Bottom: sweat gland 2 Keeps out germs, keeps out water 3 ...about 37 °C 4 By sweating 5 By shivering

2.15

1 carbohydrates, fats; proteins 2 Ticks to show the following: carbohydrate in bread; fat in cheese; protein in bread, milk, and cheese 3 Cheese, milk 4 Vegetables, bread 5 Blackcurrants, oranges 6 a) ...it is used in making bones and teeth b) ...it helps food pass through gut more easily

2.16

1 a) germs b) infection c) immune d) antibodies e) vaccine 2 From sneeze, from dirty food, from dirty hands touching food 3 So that germs on hands won't get on food

2.17

1 Sentences: 1st on left goes with 4th on right; 2nd on left goes with 5th on right; 3rd on left goes with 6th on right; 4th on left goes with 3rd on right; 5th on left goes with 1st on right; 6th on left goes with 2nd on right 2 So that they won't catch German measles during first three months of pregnancy, as this would harm baby

2.18

1 a) Four legs, one tail, two ears b) Length of legs, length of tail, colour of fur 2 B is housefly, C is earwig, D is butterfly 3 F is plantain, G is yarrow, H is rye glass

2.19

1 Ticks to show the following: all have backbones; all have lungs; fish, amphibians, and reptiles have scales; birds have feathers; mammals have fur; fish, amphibians, reptiles, and birds lay eggs; mammals have babies; birds and mammals have a steady body temperature; also H is at top of 'Mammals' column.

2.20

1 Height, hair length 2 Tom, from top: father's, mother's, mother's, mother's, mother's. Matthew, from top: mother's, mother's, mother's, mother's, father's. Jane, from top: father's, father's, father's, father's, mother's 3 Big muscles

2.21

1 a) cells (or sperms) b) genes c) chromosomes d) sperms 2 TRUE; FALSE; TRUE

2.22

1 a) frog b) polar bear c) human 2 By factory waste, sewage, and fertilizers 3 a) ...it stops it getting light and water b) ...it may eat it

2.23

1 a) Large eyes b) Large claws c) Sharp beak d) Feathers which can trap air 2 Difficult for it to be seen by animals that might eat it 3 Sentences: 1st on left goes with 4th on right; 2nd on left goes with 3rd on right; 3rd on left goes with 5th on right; 4th on left goes with 1st on right; 5th on left goes with 2nd on right

2.24

1 cabbage → caterpillar → thrush → fox 2 ...the cabbage; ...the caterpillar, thrush, and fox 3 octopus, crab, seal, seagull

2.25

1 a) Can rot b) Ticks to show that fruit, paper, cotton, and wood are biodegradable. Others are not 2 ...decomposers; ...decay, ...liquid, ...they put useful substances back into it. 3 Warmth, damp, air

2.26

1 Oxygen, carbon, nitrogen, hydrogen 2 a) Plants b) Any two of: animals, burning fires or fuels, decomposer microbes c) Coal, oil, natural gas 3 ...animals eat plants; ...they go into the soil and are taken into the roots of new, growing plants

2.27

1 ...heat; ...the Sun's ultraviolet radiation; ...fuel-burning power stations and vehicles 2 Sulphur dioxide (or nitrogen oxides) 3 Carbon dioxide, methane 4 All except 'planting more trees'

2.28

1 a) stoma b) chlorophyll c) vacuole d) xylem tube e) carbon dioxide, water e) glucose, oxygen 2 Any two of: nucleus, cytoplasm, cell membrane 3 Any two of: cell wall, choroplasts, large vacuole 4 Carbon dioxide, water, light

2.29

1 46 2 23 3 23 4 a) sexual b) asexual c) sexual 5 They inherit it 6 First row: X (sperm), X (egg), girl. Second row: Y (sperm), X (egg), boy

2.30

1 reptiles, birds, mammals 2 a) Because its long neck gives it an advantage in getting food b) Because they have all inherited the long neck from the surviving animal in the second picture 3 a) extinction b) mutation c) adaptation

2.31

1 a) 950 kJ b) 1650 kJ c) 4400 kJ 2 If energy is not needed, food is turned into fat 3 Bumps on surface of small intestine; they absorb digested food into the blood 4 Carried by blood to liver 5 Pyramid similar to left-hand example on p75 6 Pyramid similar to right-hand example on p75, with these biomasses: frogs 200 g, worms 10 000 g, leaves 500 000 g

3.1

1 Ticks and crosses to show the following: solid has fixed shape, fixed volume, and can't flow; liquid has fixed shape, no fixed volume, and can flow; gas has no fixed shape, no fixed volume, and can flow **2** a) petrol b) lead, gold c) air d) water **3** a) 1000 b) 2

3.2

1 0 °C; 100 °C **2** liquid; gas; solid; liquid **3** So that there is room for expansion on a hot day

3.3

1 a) brittle b) flexible c) transparent d) malleable **2** Examples of materials (from top): glass, PVC (plastic), glass, copper, copper, wood, PVC **3** a) strong, flexible b) heat insulator c) electrical insulator, strong d) flexible

3.4

1 metals; atoms; metals; nonmetals; compounds **2** hydrogen, oxygen, carbon, nitrogen, sulphur **3** Table: water is made from hydrogen and oxygen; carbon dioxide is made from carbon and oxygen; sulphuric acid is made from hydrogen, oxygen, and sulphur

3.5

1 a) pure substance b) alloy **2** dissolves; soluble; solvent; solution

3.6

1 a) dissolving and filtering b) dissolving and filtering c) filtering, or distilling d) chromatography **2** Tea-leaves, liquid tea (mainly water) **3** Dust, air

3.7

1 From top: acid, acid, alkali, acid, alkali, acid, alkali, alkali, acid, alkali **2** a) dilute b) concentrated c) hydrogen d) ...it has cancelled out the acid effect e) ...does not change colour

3.8

1 a) gas b) liquid c) solid **2** nucleus; protons, neutrons; electrons; eight; two, two

3.9

1 a) chemical b) chemical c) physical **2** From top: chemical, physical, physical, chemical, chemical, physical, chemical

3.10

1 a) carbon dioxide b) oxygen c) carbon dioxide d) methane e) oxygen f) carbon dioxide g) carbon dioxide **2** air (oxygen), heat, fuel

3.11

1 a) water b) hydrogen c) carbon dioxide **2** a) sulphuric acid, zinc b) zinc sulphate, hydrogen c) zinc sulphate

3.12

1 a) aluminium b) copper c) copper d) gold e) iron f) iron g) gold h) gold **2** air, water **3** coating with paint, coating with grease

3.13

1 a) Iron, carbon b) Blast furnace **2** Sentence order is 2nd, 4th, 3rd, 1st **3** a) Iron, carbon b) Chromium, nickel c) Making steel, making cast iron

3.14

1 ...quarries **2** a) chippings b) concrete c) cement d) quicklime e) glass **3** In making cement, as chippings

3.15

1 a) hydrocarbon b) fractionating tower c) polymerization d) distillation e) cracking **2** Any two of: petrol, jet fuel, paraffin, diesel, heating oil, bottled gas, **3** PVC, polythene, or any two plastics in the diagram on p105 **4** Detergents, polishes, or any two 'Others' in the diagram on p105

3.16

1 a) nitrogen b) oxygen c) carbon dioxide d) nitrogen **2** a) Helium, ...it is lighter than other gases in air b) Carbon dioxide, ...things can't burn in it c) Nitrogen, ...it doesn't make food go bad **3** Neon, used in some lamps

3.17

1 a and b) ammonia c, d, and e) ammonium nitrate **2** ...they need to replace the nitrates and other minerals taken away with the crops **3** Polluting drinking water, making more green algae grow in ponds and streams

3.18

1 Sentence order is 1st, 3rd, 6th, 5th, 4th, 2nd **2** By running into river, then sea, then evaporating; by going into plants, then evaporating **3** ...water vapour condenses on cold ground or plants; ...frost; ...water expands when it freezes

3.19

1 a) erosion b) sediment c) humus **2** Sentence order is 4th, 5th, 3rd, 1st, 2nd

3.20

1 a) sedimentary b) igneous c) metamorphic **2** granite (igneous) used for chippings; limestone (sedimentary) used in cement; slate (metamorphic) used in snooker tables

3.21

1 a) Strata b) Crust **2** A, ...the lower layer of sediment was deposited first **3** ...they buckle when huge pieces of crust move together; ...igneous rocks are formed from material which was molten (melted)

3.22

1 a) lava b) crust c) core d) plate **2** a) ...rocks slide or push against each other at plate edges b) ..they were once joined together as one giant continent

3.23

1 a) 2 b) 8 c) 8 **2** a) For shells 1, 2, 3, 4, numbers are: argon 2, 8, 8, 0; potassium 2, 8, 8, 1 b) Argon; because it has a full outer shell **3** Sodium ion has lost an electron, so it is positively charged **4** a) 3 b) Lithium-6 has 3 electrons, 3 protons, 3 neutrons. Lithium-7 has 3 electrons, 3 protrons, 4 neutrons

3.24

1 a) fluorine b) potassium c) cobalt d) krypton e) oxygen **2** Any three Group 1 elements, e.g. lithium, sodium, potassium **3** Any three Group 7 elements, e.g. fluorine, chlorine, bromine **4** Any three noble gases, e.g. helium, neon, argon **5** Low density, reactive metals **6** unreactive, colourless gases

3.25

1 a) Sodium chloride b) Any two listed in the diagram on p125 2 a) sodium b) copper c) All except copper d) sodium, aluminium 3 a) sodium hydroxide b) sodium sulphate c) sodium hydroxide d) 7

3.26

1 a) Copper; iron b) Iron 2 a) Gas b) Reaction is reversible c) 3 Any three of: smaller bits, higher temperature, greater concentration of reactants, adding catalyst 4 Enzymes are catalyst for reaction that makes alcohol from glucose

3.27

1 a) Oceans hold water which was once water vapour b) There are plants to give out oxygen 2 a) K b) J c) M d) N e) L 3 Because sedimentary rock will be changed by heat from magma 4 Sedimentary rock buried, then melted to become magma which might collect under a volcano

4.1

1 positive; negative; negative; positive; negative 2 Ticks to show the following: copper, aluminium, and carbon are good conductors; water and air are poor conductors; plastic and glass are insulators

4.2

1 ammeter; current; current 2 ...a voltmeter; ...an ammeter; ...2.0

4.3

1 a) B b) Because the voltage across it is higher, so the current through it is higher 2 a) C b) D c) It will go out d) It will stay bright

4.4

1 a) resistance b) heat c) power d) kilowatt 2 A, ...there is less resistance in the circuit

4.5

1 south; north; north 2 Ticks to show the following: nickel, iron, and steel are magnetic, aluminium and copper are non-magnetic 3 a) Steel b) Iron c) Iron

4.6

1 a) The needle of the meter moves one way b) The needle of the meter moves the opposite way 2 a) alternating current b) alternator c) transformer

4.7

1 earth, green and yellow; neutral, blue; live, brown 2 a) ...the current would be too high for the fuse, so the fuse would blow b) ...a fault might produce a current high enough to cause overheating, but not high enough to blow the fuse

4.8

1 weight; friction; tension; air resistance 2 newton 3 Force of 6 N downwards from centre of ball

4.9

1 a) low b) high c) high d) low 2 newtons per square metre 3 a) 2 b) 2 N/m²

4.10

1 Sentence order is 5th, 4th, 2nd, 3rd, 1st 2 a) ...increases b) ...in all directions c) ...an upthrust from the water d) ...a liquid

4.11

1 A, ...it is longer 2 ...she is lighter than person A 3 Y, ...its centre of gravity is not over the table underneath, so its weight has a turning effect which will pull it over

4.12

1 speed; 20; 40 2 From top: useful, useful, problem, useful, problem, useful 3 Streamlined helmet, streamlined frame, streamlined wheels, crouching position

4.13

1 joules; forms 2 Examples, from top: torch beam, moving car, petrol, stretched spring

4.14

1 TRUE; FALSE 2 hot water bottle; plant; hairdrier; candle

4.15

1 ...insulators; ...it traps air 2 Good conductors: silver, copper, aluminium. Insulators: glass, wood, air, plastic foam 3 Wool in gloves, fibre filling in coats 4 Plastic foam round hot water tanks, plastic handles on saucepans 5 Labels: convection (top), cool (left), hot (right)

4.16

1 a) LESS b) MORE c) LESS d) MORE 2 a) radiation b) radiation c) convection

4.17

1 Sentence order is 3rd, 2nd, 5th, 1st, 4th 2 fuel-burning; nuclear, tidal, wind, and hydroelectric; tidal and hydroelectric

4.18

1 Sentence order is 4th, 3rd, 5th, 2nd, 1st 2 'yes' and 'no' to show the following: coal, oil, and natural gas are fossil fuels; wood and alcohol are renewable

4.20

1 a) air b) vacuum c) oscilloscope d) vibrations 2 ...about 330 metres per second; ...300 000 kilometres per second; ...the light travels much faster than the sound

4.21

1 Sentence order is 2nd, 4th, 3rd, 5th, 1st 2 higher; louder

4.22

1 a) echo b) ultrasound 2 Echo sounders in boats, ultrasound scanning in hospitals 3 a) ...the depth of water underneath it b) ...deeper

4.23

1 Two straight lines should leave bulb, touch ball either side, and reach screen; shadow area on screen is between these two lines 2 Ray should reflect from mirror at same angle as it arrives, then go into eye; image of pencil is below mirror, and in a position which exactly matches that of pencil above mirror 3 ...it reflects light into your eyes

4.24

1 a) transparent b) refraction 2 Ray should bend downwards slightly as it goes into glass (as in diagram on p176; ray should bend again as it leaves glass, so that its direction is parallel to the direction it first had (see also diagram on p176) 3 ...becomes less

4.25

1 A Ray is reflected as in top diagram on p178 B Ray is reflected as in centre left diagram on p178 C Ray zig-zags along fibre as in bottom diagram on p178 **2** C is the optical fibre **3** Carrying telephone signals, viewing inside the body

4.26

1 Rays should be as in diagrams at top of p180 **2** convex; concave; convex; convex; convex **3** ...the film; ...the retina

4.27

1 ...a prism; ...a spectrum **2** a) red b) red, green, and blue c) red d) black e) green and blue

4.28

1 light **2** radio waves, microwaves, infrared, light, ultraviolet, X-rays, gamma rays **3** a) X-rays (or gamma rays) b) gamma rays c) microwaves d) ultraviolet e) light f) radio waves (or microwaves) g) infrared

4.29

1 a) nuclear radiation b) GM tube c) gamma rays d) alpha particles e) alpha particles f) gamma rays g) gamma rays **2** ...it can damage or kill living cells

4.30

1 24 hours; 365 days; 365 days; 24 hours **2** a) Right half of Earth should be in shadow (edge of shadow should be vertical) b) night c) winter

4.31

1 380 000; 28; 28 **2** a) Sun b) Moon, Sun **3** Communications, navigation, watching the weather

4.32

1 Jupiter; Mercury; Mercury; Pluto; Pluto; Saturn; Mercury; Pluto **2** Gravity

4.33

1 a) star b) nebula c) galaxy d) Universe **2** a) 4 years b) 100 000 years c) 2 million d) Over 100 billion

4.34

1 a) 4 Ω b) 36 W **2** 2 A **3** 24 V **4** Top meter 8 V; right meter 2 A

4.35

1 a) More coils, higher voltage battery, iron core b) Connect battery other way round **2** a) Switching off a circuit if the current gets too high b) Increasing the voltage of AC **3** a) Upward force greater b) Force acts downwards **4** Force from electromagnet becomes strong enough to move catch so that spring can pull contacts apart

4.36

1 4 m/s **2** 2 m/s^2 **3** 6 N **4** 200 Pa (or N/m^2) **5** b) Point is at 27 mm extension c) 2.3 N

4.37

1 100 J **2** 10 W **3** a) 8 kW h b) 80p c) 160p

4.38

1 a) 36 mm b) 15 mm **2** 5 kHz **3** 100 000 000 **4** Because they can kill or damage living cells **5** a) ultraviolet, gamma rays b) radio waves, infrared, ultraviolet, gamma rays

GCSE questions (pages 211-216)

1 **a** 9 **b** 4 **c** His father

2 **a** i) Causes bowel disease (or constipation, too much weight) ii) Causes heart disease (or lung disease) **b** 'Burns off' weight (or strengthens heart muscles, helps blood circulation)

3 **a** i) C ii) D iii) E iv) A **b** light, water (or minerals) **c** Can't take in water, can't take in minerals **d** i) pea plant $\rightarrow$ greenfly $\rightarrow$ ladybird ii) Ladybird is the predator iii) If ladybirds are killed, greenfly population will increase **e** A is chloroplast, B is cytoplasm (or stored food, in cytoplasm), C is cell wall, D is cell membrane

4 Letter order is G, D, B, A, F, C, E

5 **a** Sulphur dioxide, nitrogen oxides, (or water vapour) **b** Sulphur dioxide and nitrogen oxides dissolve in rainwater and cause acid rain which harms plants, water life, and stonework

6 **a** Igneous **b** E **c** Cooled more quickly, so crystals had less time to form

7 air, oxygen, chemical change, gases, carbon dioxide, water vapour, heat energy

8 **a** sodium **b** chlorine **c** copper (or gold) **d** copper sulphate **e** fluorine **f** sodium hydroxide

9 **a** C **b** E **c** B **d** A **e** D

10 **a** i) Sugar (or glucose syrup) ii) Citric acid **b** i) Sodium ii) 4

11 **a** B **b** year, day

12 **a** i) S_3 ii) All three switches **b** i) It rises ii) To stop heaters overheating **c** i) Brown, blue ii) Earth iii) It has a plastic case, so is double-insulated **d** i) 1300 W ii) Length of time it is switched on for

13 **a** light **b** ultraviolet **c** microwaves **d** X-rays **e** infrared

14 **a** i) Oil (or natural gas) ii) From remains of plants and tiny sea creatures which were trapped in sediment millions of years ago iii) Something that supplies energy, when burnt for example iv) Wood (or nuclear fuel) **b** Resource that cannot be replaced when used up

15 **a** i) 0.5 m^2 ii) 2 m^2 **b** 50 000 N/m^2 (Pa)

16 **a** Jupiter **b** Venus **c** Mercury **d** Venus

Edexcel Foundation, London Examinations accepts no responsibility whatsoever for the accuracy or method of working in the answers given.

Index

Periodic table

Group

Period	Group 1	Group 2	transition metals											Group 3	Group 4	Group 5	Group 6	Group 7	Group 0
1	H hydrogen 1																		He helium 2
2	Li lithium 3	Be beryllium 4												B boron 5	C carbon 6	N nitrogen 7	O oxygen 8	F flourine 9	Ne neon 10
3	Na sodium 11	Mg magnesium 12												Al aluminium 13	Si silicon 14	P phosphorus 15	S sulphur 16	Cl chlorine 17	Ar argon 18
4	K potassium 19	Ca calcium 20	Sc scandium 21	Ti titanium 22	V vandium 23	Cr chromium 24	Mn manganese 25	Fe iron 26	Co cobalt 27	Ni nickel 28	Cu copper 29	Zn zinc 30	Ga gallium 31	Ge germanium 32	As arsenic 33	Se selenium 34	Br bromine 35	Kr krypton 36
5	Rb rubidium 37	Sr strontium 38	Y yttrium 39	Zr zirconium 40	Nb niobium 41	Mo molybdenum 42	Tc technetium 43	Ru ruthenium 44	Rh rhodium 45	Pd palladium 46	Ag silver 47	Cd cadmium 48	In indium 49	Sn tin 50	Sb antimony 51	Te tellurium 52	I iodine 53	Xe xenon 54
6	Cs caesium 55	Ba barium 56	La lanthanum 57	Hf hafnium 58	Ta tantalum 73	W tungsten 74	Re rhenium 75	Os osmium 76	Ir iridium 77	Pt platinum 78	Au gold 79	Hg mercury 80	Tl thallium 81	Pb lead 82	Bi bismuth 83	Po polonium 84	At astatine 85	Rn radon 86
7	Fr francium 87	Ra radium 88	Ac actinium 89															

Ce cerium 58	Pr praseodymium 59	Nd neodymium 60	Pm promethium 61	Sm samarium 62	Eu europium 63	Gd gadolinium 64	Tb terbium 65	Dy dysprosium 67	Ho holmium 68	Er erbium 69	Tm thulium 70	Yb ytterbium 71	Lu lutetium 72
Th thorium 90	Pa protactinium 91	U uranium 92	Np neptunium 93	Pu plutonium 94	Am americium 95	Cm curium 96	Bk berkelium 97	Cf californium 98	Es einsteinium 99	Fm fermium 100	Md mendelevium 101	No nobelium 102	Lr lawrencium 103